DAILY LANGUAGE PRACTICE

by Isaac Seder

Daily Language Practice provides a structured approach to building and reviewing your students' language and literacy skills. Each of the 36 weeks includes daily, weekly, and monthly activities.

Weekly Skill
Practice one skill each week

Monthly Review
Apply skills learned each month

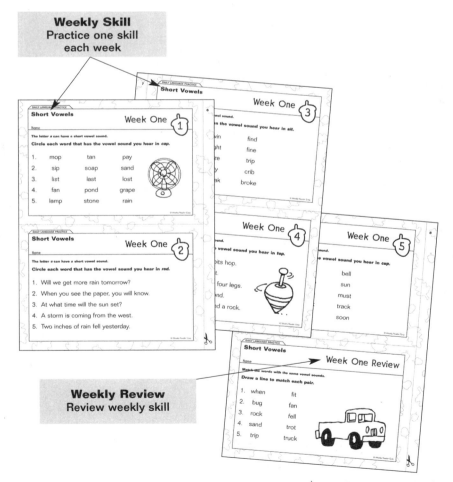

Weekly Review
Review weekly skill

1 2 3 4 5 / 10 09 08 07 06

Table of Contents

Skills: Scope and Sequence

The Scope and Sequence chart on this page provides a complete overview of the skills reviewed in this book. Use this chart to select practice activities that cover skills you are currently teaching or to review previously taught skills.

Skill	W1	W2	W3	W4	W5	W6	W7	W8	W9	W10	W11	W12	W13	W14	W15	W16	W17	W18	W19	W20	W21	W22	W23	W24	W25	W26	W27	W28	W29	W30	W31	W32	W33	W34	W35	W36
Punctuation & Capitalization																																				
Sentences		X																																		
Commas																														X						
Apostrophes																	X				X														X	
Capitalization		X												X									X											X		
Grammar																																				
Identifying Nouns			X																																	
Plural Nouns					X																								X							
Articles						X																														
Identifying Verbs										X																										
Subject-Verb Agreement														X										X												
Complete Sentences															X																					
Possessive Nouns																	X																			X
Verb Forms (Adding Suffixes)																		X			X															
Contractions																						X														X
Identifying Adjectives																												X								
Pronouns																																	X			
Vocabulary																																				
Synonyms											X																									
Compound Words										X																										
Antonyms																				X																
Reading Skills																																				
Short Vowel Sounds	X																																			
Rhyming Words			X																							X										
Long Vowel Sounds				X																																
Alphabetical Order																			X																	
Spelling																																				
Double Letters								X																												
Long a											X																									
Long e and i														X																						
Long o and u																X																				
R-Controlled Vowels																							X													
Consonant Blends																												X								
Homophones																															X					
Commonly Misspelled Words																																				X

Using this Book

Daily Practice

This reproducible book provides daily language practice with many essential second-grade language arts skills. You can use these quick activities in a variety of classroom situations—as daily warm-ups, quick assessment tools, or helpful reviews.

The book's organization features 36 weekly practice sessions centered around a single topic, followed by a monthly review of the skills covered during the previous four weeks. This approach allows for in-depth and focused practice of essential language arts concepts in a concentrated time frame. Whenever appropriate, the exercises use material from *Weekly Reader®* magazine. This engaging resource provides high-interest content and skill practice in context.

The exercises offered for the first part of each week are simpler. These afford students the opportunity to experience success while practicing previously introduced skills. As the week progresses, the activities gradually become more challenging. Likewise, the more complex skills are offered as the year progresses.

When planning your daily routine, try one or more of these management techniques:

• Distribute copies of each daily page to individual students or to small groups. You might choose to have students work together for Day One through Day Three and then individually for Days Four and Five. When students work independently, encourage them to exchange work with a partner and compare and discuss their answers. Or, review the correct responses together as a large group.

• Use an overhead projector or create transparencies to complete the work in a large group. Ask volunteers to help complete each item. Try completing Day One as a whole-class activity to review the week's skill. Then have students work independently or in pairs throughout the week.

• Direct students to complete the activity pages for homework. Encourage students to discuss their work with their families.

Weekly Reviews

There is a weekly review to reinforce the work of the previous days. Many of the weekly reviews use a "Find the Mistakes" format that allows students to practice identifying errors in context. You can use this review as an assessment, collecting and scoring each student's work individually. You might prefer to use this skills review as an assessment tool to determine weak areas or gaps in your students' knowledge.

Monthly Reviews

At the end of each four-week set, there is an activity page that reviews the skills taught during that month. Each monthly review includes a "Find the Mistakes" activity or a fun word game.

Skills Overview

The Scope and Sequence chart on the previous page provides a complete overview of the skills reviewed in this book. Use this chart to select practice activities that cover skills you are currently teaching or to review previously taught skills.

Short Vowels

Week One

1

Name

The letter _a_ can have a short vowel sound.

Circle each word that has the vowel sound you hear in _cap._

1. mop   tan   pay
2. sip   soap   sand
3. list   last   lost
4. fan   pond   grape
5. lamp   stone   rain

Short Vowels

Week One

2

Name

The letter _e_ can have a short vowel sound.

Circle each word that has the vowel sound you hear in _red._

1. Will we get more rain tomorrow?
2. When you see the paper, you will know.
3. At what time will the sun set?
4. A storm is coming from the west.
5. Two inches of rain fell yesterday.

Short Vowels

Week One

3

Name

The letter *i* can have a short vowel sound.

Circle each word that has the vowel sound you hear in *sit.*

1.	look	win	find
2.	fit	fight	fine
3.	trunk	size	trip
4.	creep	cry	crib
5.	brick	break	broke

Short Vowels

Week One

4

Name

The letter *o* can have a short vowel sound.

Circle each word that has the vowel sound you hear in *top.*

1. Worms crawl and rabbits hop.

2. Horses sometimes trot.

3. A lot of animals run on four legs.

4. Some fish swim in a pond.

5. A snake can slide around a rock.

Short Vowels

Week One

5

Name

The letter _u_ can have a short vowel sound.

Circle each word that has the vowel sound you hear in _cup._

1.	bee	bug	bell
2.	tune	soup	sun
3.	me	mine	must
4.	trick	truck	track
5.	fun	rude	soon

Short Vowels

Week One Review

Name

Match the words with the same vowel sounds. Draw a line to match each pair.

1.	when	fit
2.	bug	fan
3.	rock	fell
4.	sand	trot
5.	trip	truck

Sentences

Week Two

1

Name

Use a period (.) at the end of a statement. Use a question mark (?) at the end of a question.

Complete each sentence. Add a period (.) or a question mark (?).

1. Some butterflies migrate in the fall_____

2. Where do the butterflies go_____

3. Do whales migrate_____

4. A tern is a kind of bird_____

5. Terns fly from the North Pole to the South Pole_____

Sentences

Week Two

2

Name

Begin every sentence with a capital letter.

Choose the correct word.

1. _____ moon is a large rock.
   the   The

2. _____ travels around Earth.
   It   it

3. _____ was the first person on the moon?
   Who   who

4. _____ 1969, Neil Armstrong walked on the moon.
   in   In

5. _____ from the sun makes the moon bright.
   light   Light

Sentences

Week Two

3

Name

Use a period (.) at the end of a statement. Use a question mark (?) at the end of a question.

Complete each sentence. Add a period (.) or a question mark (?).

1. What is a tadpole_____

2. A tadpole is a young frog_____

3. Tadpoles swim in the water_____

4. How do tadpoles change_____

5. They begin to grow legs_____

© Weekly Reader Corp.

Sentences

Week Two

4

Name

Use a period (.) at the end of a statement. Use a question mark (?) at the end of a question.

Complete each sentence. Add a period (.) or a question mark (?).

1. Apples are fruits that grow on trees_____

2. Apple trees grow from seeds_____

3. Where can you find the roots of a tree_____

4. Why do apples float_____

5. They float because they contain air_____

© Weekly Reader Corp.

Sentences

Week Two

5

Begin every sentence with a capital letter. Use a period (.) at the end of a statement. Use a question mark (?) at the end of a question.

Correct each sentence.

1. some Native Americans fished for food.

   _____

2. Many Native Americans made baskets for storage

   _____

3. what were tepees?

   _____

4. Tepees are cone-shaped homes made with tree bark

   _____

Sentences

Week Two Review

Find the mistakes. Write each sentence correctly on the line.

1. Scorpions have fangs and stingers

   _____

2. where do most scorpions live

   _____

3. They live in deserts around the world?

   _____

4. how many legs does a scorpion have.

   _____

5. a scorpion has eight legs

   _____

Nouns

Week Three

1

Name

A noun names a person, place, or thing.

Circle the noun in each pair.

1. red   ball
2. house   big
3. water   swim
4. think   brain
5. friend   friendly

Nouns

Week Three

2

Name

A noun names a person, place, or thing.

Circle the nouns in each sentence.

1. A candle drips wax.

2. The flame burns brightly.

3. Some cakes have candles.

4. Be careful with matches!

5. Fire can be very dangerous.

DAILY LANGUAGE PRACTICE

Nouns

Week Three 3

Name

A noun names a person, place, or thing.

Is it a noun? Write *Yes* or *No.*

_______ 1. climb

_______ 2. Brooklyn Bridge

_______ 3. Mr. Lopez

_______ 4. island

_______ 5. sad

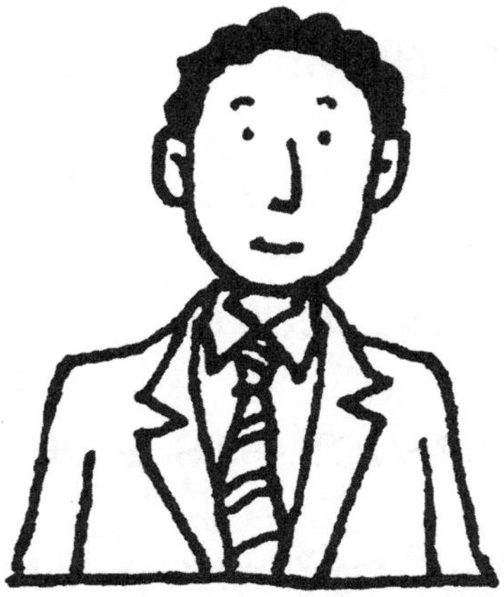

DAILY LANGUAGE PRACTICE

Nouns

Week Three 4

Name

A noun names a person, place, or thing.

Circle the nouns.

1.	clam	wet	shell
2.	crab	pinch	Pacific Ocean
3.	Cape Cod	river	boat
4.	soft	Miami Beach	brown
5.	rock	pebble	stone

Nouns

Week Three

5

Name

A noun names a person, place, or thing.

Circle the nouns.

1. People like to visit the park.

2. Wind blows through the trees.

3. Some leaves fall to the ground.

4. The workers sweep with rakes.

5. Now the paths are clear.

Nouns

Week Three Review

Name

A noun names a person, place, or thing.

Circle the nouns.

1. The zipper was invented in 1913.

2. The inventor was Gideon Sundback.

3. This clever man lived in Canada.

4. Zippers began to replace buttons.

5. Some pants, jackets, and coats use zippers.

DAILY LANGUAGE PRACTICE

Rhyming Words

Week Four 1

Name

Rhyming words have the same end sounds.

Circle the rhyming words.

1.	map	man	cap
2.	day	dog	log
3.	sun	rug	run
4.	sky	why	me
5.	tree	trip	ship

DAILY LANGUAGE PRACTICE

Rhyming Words

Week Four 2

Name

Rhyming words have the same end sounds.

Do the words rhyme? Write *Yes* or *No.*

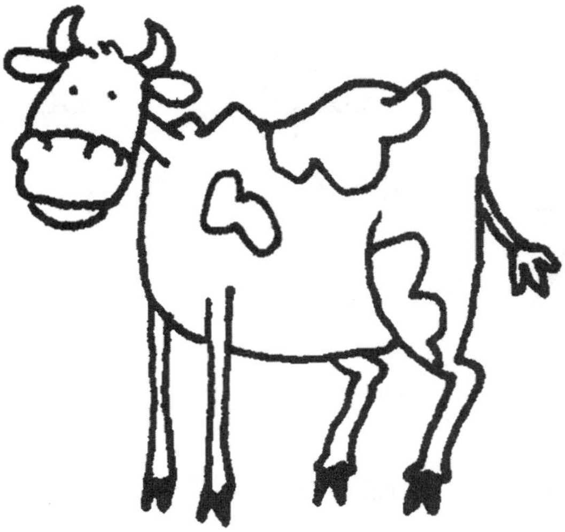

______	1.	pen	hen
______	2.	sit	sip
______	3.	play	day
______	4.	boy	toy
______	5.	more	moo

Rhyming Words

Week Four

3

Name _____

Rhyming words have the same end sounds.

Write a word that rhymes.

1. fish   w_____

2. save   c_____

3. fill   sp_____

4. hope   r_____

5. dress   m_____

Rhyming Words

Week Four

4

Name _____

Rhyming words have the same end sounds.

Circle the rhyming words

1.   fox   boy   box

2.   grade   made   gray

3.   tin   ring   sing

4.   cuts   let   nuts

5.   pen   bend   send

Rhyming Words

Week Four

5

Name

Rhyming words have the same end sounds. Match the rhyming words.

Draw a line between two words that rhyme.

1. chick   spell

2. bell   soon

3. near   plate

4. moon   brick

5. late   hear

Rhyming Words

Week Four Review

Name

Circle the rhyming words in each sentence.

1. The moon is soon full.

2. Do you know why the sky gets dark at night?

3. She can ring a bell and sing at the same time.

4. We hope the rope will be strong.

5. The sun helps the team run faster.

Monthly Review

Name _____

A. Find the mistakes. Rewrite the sentences in the correct form.

1. Do you know what Kwanzaa is.

_____

2. it is an African American holiday

_____

3. kwanzaa lasts for seven nights

_____

4. What do people do during this holiday.

_____

5. they share food, stories, and traditions

_____

B. Find five nouns. Go across and down. Write them on the lines.

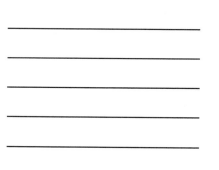

T	R	E	E	C
H	A	C	G	H
D	B	Y	G	E
I	B	O	H	R
R	I	V	E	R
M	T	P	V	Y

_____

_____

_____

_____

_____

C. Choose a word from the box to complete each sentence.

> pool   yell   yes   wish   will

1. *Spill* rhymes with _____.
2. *Spend* has the same vowel sound as _____.
3. *Spell* rhymes with _____.
4. *Spin* has the same vowel sound as _____.
5. *Spool* rhymes with _____.

Long Vowel Sounds

Week Five

1

Name

You can hear the long *a* sound in many words.

Circle each word that has the vowel sound you hear in *cake*.

1.   date   set   coat

2.   goat   game   grin

3.   rain   home   time

4.   please   plus   plane

5.   eight   nine   ten

Long Vowel Sounds

Week Five

2

Name

You can hear the long *e* sound in many words.

Circle each word that has the vowel sound you hear in *meet*.

1. A baseball team has nine players.

2. Baseball can be played on a field.

3. The grass there is usually green.

4. Each player has a turn at bat.

5. Did you see the batter hit a home run?

Long Vowel Sounds

Week Five

③

Name

You can hear the long *i* sound in many words.

Circle each word that has the vowel sound you hear in *lime*.

1.   fur   fin   fine

2.   loop   lot   light

3.   real   ride   rich

4.   why   we   who

5.   leap   lay   lie

Long Vowel Sounds

Week Five

④

Name

You can hear the long *o* sound in many words.

Circle each word that has the vowel sound you hear in *joke*.

1. Cars drive on a road.

2. Many people park their cars at home.

3. Fog lights help to show the way when it rains.

4. A tow truck can pull a car that will not run.

5. Some people go to work by train.

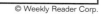

Long Vowel Sounds

Week Five

5

Name

You can hear the long _u_ sound in many words.

Circle each word that has the vowel sound you hear in _tune._

1. mail   mule   mile

2. spoon   spy   spell

3. rust   rude   rich

4. so   son   moon

5. lick   near   blue

Long Vowel Sounds

Week Five Review

Name

Draw a line between words that have the same vowel sounds.

1. game   stream

2. spoon   noon

3. home   date

4. team   time

5. ride   hole

Plural Nouns

Week Six

1

Name _____

A plural noun names more than one person, place, or thing.

Circle the plural nouns.

1. Plants collect water through their roots.

2. Leaves grow on plant stems.

3. Fruits and vegetables grow from seeds.

4. Gardens need sunlight.

5. Heavy winds can damage crops.

Plural Nouns

Week Six

2

Name _____

Add –s to form many plural nouns.

Write the plural noun.

1. 1 star 2 _____

2. 1 planet 2 _____

3. 1 moon 2 _____

4. 1 rocket 2 _____

5. 1 comet 2 _____

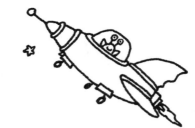

Plural Nouns

Week Six

③

Name

Add –s to form many plural nouns. Add –es to form other plural nouns.

Choose the correct word.

1. Many _____ are covered with sand.
   beachs   beaches

2. Waves are caused by _____.
   tides   tidez

3. Some _____ cannot grow near the ocean.
   bushes   bushs

4. The salt in the water can damage _____.
   plantz   plants

5. Empty _____ wash up on the shore.
   shelles   shells

Plural Nouns

Week Six

④

Name

Add –s to form many plural nouns. Add –es to form other plural nouns.

Write the plural of each noun.

1. home   _____

2. school   _____

3. church   _____

4. class   _____

5. building   _____

Plural Nouns

Week Six

⑤

Name

Add –s to form many plural nouns. Add –es to form other plural nouns.

Circle the correct word.

1. A tailor can sew (dresss, dresses).

2. (Tailors, Tailores) begin with a pattern.

3. Some (patternes, patterns) have (dozenz, dozens) of (piece, pieces).

4. Sewing (machinez, machines) help people sew quickly.

5. The final (touchs, touches) might be some (buttons, buttonz), (ribbons, ribbonz), or (bowz, bows).

Plural Nouns

Week Six Review

Name

Find the mistakes. Write each sentence correctly on the line.

1. The rabbits might be hiding behind the bushs.

2. The noises of machinez can scare animals.

3. Many buildinges have gardens filled with flowers.

4. Starz can be seen when there are few clouds.

5. Some churchs ring their bells at sunset.

Articles

Week Seven

1

Name

Use *a* before words that begin with a consonant.
Use *an* before words that begin with a vowel.

Choose the correct word.

1. _____ eagle is a bird of prey
       A   An

2. _____ bird of prey hunts other animals.
       A   An

3. _____ ostrich is not a bird of prey.
       A   An

4. The ostrich is _____ flightless bird.
           a   an

Articles

Week Seven

2

Name

Use *a* before words that begin with a consonant.
Use *an* before words that begin with a vowel.

Write *a* or *an* to complete each sentence.

1. Have you seen _____ rainbow?

2. Rainbows usually are shaped like _____ arch.

3. Rainbows sometimes appear after _____ storm.

4. _____ interesting story says there is gold at the end of the rainbow.

5. However, this is only _____ legend.

Articles

Week Seven

③

Name

Use *a* before words that begin with a consonant.
Use *an* before words that begin with a vowel.

Find the mistakes. Write each sentence correctly on the line.

1. A elephant is a mammal.

   _____

2. All mammals have an backbone.

   _____

3. A eel is not a mammal.

   _____

4. It is an kind of fish.

   _____

Articles

Week Seven

④

Name

Use *a* before words that begin with a consonant.
Use *an* before words that begin with a vowel.

Choose the correct word.

1. _____ glacier is _____ river of ice.
      A   An   a   an

2. Sometimes _____ iceberg breaks off of a glacier.
               a   an

3. _____ large part of the iceberg is under water.
      A   An

4. Some icebergs are _____ bright blue color.
              a   an

Articles

Week Seven

(5)

Name _____

Use *a* before words that begin with a consonant.
Use *an* before words that begin with a vowel.

Write *a* or *an* to complete each sentence.

1. Golf is _____ popular game.

2. Players use _____ club to hit _____ ball.

3. Miniature golf is _____ easy game to learn.

4. To hit the ball softly, give it _____ light tap.

5. _____ early version of golf was played in 1350!

Articles

Week Seven Review

Name _____

Use *a* before words that begin with a consonant. Use *an* before words that begin with a vowel.

Find the mistakes. Write each sentence correctly on the line.

1. Mexico is an country in North America.
   _____

2. A eagle appears on the Mexican flag.
   _____

3. The eagle is eating an snake.
   _____

4. The flag also has an green, a red, and white stripe.
   _____

5. The name Mexico comes from a Aztec word.

Spelling (Double Letters)

Week Eight

1

Name _____

Some words are spelled with double letters.

Circle the word that is spelled correctly.

1. well   wel

2. ful   full

3. spil   spill

4. ladder   lader

5. sily   silly

Spelling (Double Letters)

Week Eight

2

Name _____

Some words are spelled with double letters.

Choose the word that is spelled correctly.

1. A pony is a _____ horse.
   smal   small

2. Some ponies are very _____.
   little   litle

3. Horses are _____ than ponies.
   taler   taller

4. Some ponies snack on _____.
   carots   carrots

5. Other ponies like to chew _____.
   gras   grass

Spelling (Double Letters)

Week Eight

(3)

Name

Some words are spelled with double letters.

Circle the word that is NOT spelled correctly and write it correctly on the line.

1. Some kids take music lesons.

   _____

2. They might take a clas to play the piano.

   _____

3. The more you practice, the better you wil play.

   _____

4. Playing music can make people feel hapy.

   _____

© Weekly Reader Corp.

Spelling (Double Letters)

Week Eight

(4)

Name

Some words are spelled with double letters.

Circle the word that is spelled correctly.

1. buble   bubble

2. suny   sunny

3. pretty   prety

4. wal   wall

5. midle   middle

© Weekly Reader Corp.

Spelling (Double Letters)

Week Eight

⑤

Name

Some words are spelled with double letters.

Choose the word that is spelled correctly.

1. A _____ is a useful tool.
   hammer   hamer

2. A carpenter might also use a _____.
   drill   dril

3. A _____ helps you reach high places.
   ladder   lader

4. Tools can help you make a _____ bank.
   pigy   piggy

5. You can drop a _____ in your new bank.
   penny   peny

Spelling (Double Letters)

Week Eight Review

Name

Find the mistakes. Write each sentence correctly on the line.

1. Read a recipe wel before you begin to cook.
   _____

2. A teaspoon is a smal amount.
   _____

3. You can take cooking lesons at some schools.
   _____

4. A clas can teach you about safety in the kitchen.
   _____

5. Be sure to clean up anything you spil.
   _____

Monthly Review

Name _____

②

A. Find the mistakes. Write each sentence correctly on the line.

1. An beetle is usually smal.

   _____

2. However, the Goliath beetle can be six inchs long.

   _____

3. These beetlez make a awful lot of noise when they fly.

   _____

4. Some people wil tel you they sound like helicopters!

   _____

B. Choose a word from the box to answer each question. Write your answer on the little lines. The circled letters spell the answer to the riddle!

| yellow   room   sleep   penny   kite   maze |

1. Which word has the vowel sound you hear in *sky*?

   ___ ___ (___) ___

2. Which word rhymes with *days*?

   ___ (___) ___ ___

3. Which word has the vowel sound you hear in *team*?

   ___ (___) ___ ___ ___

4. Which word names a color?

   ___ ___ (___) ___ ___ ___

5. Which word names a coin?

   ___ (___) ___ ___ ___

6. Which word has the vowel sound you hear in *tune*?

   (___) ___ ___ ___

   What do most farm kids grow every year?

   (___) (___) (___) (___) (___) (___)

Synonyms

Week Nine

1

Name

Synonyms are words that have the same meaning.

Do these words have the same meaning?
Write *Yes* or *No* on the line.

_____	1. big	large
_____	2. sad	unhappy
_____	3. angry	nice
_____	4. fast	quick
_____	5. asleep	awake

Synonyms

Week Nine

2

Name

Synonyms are words that have the same meaning.

Circle the words that have the same meaning.

1. couch   sink   sofa

2. look   see   roll

3. gift   story   present

4. house   yard   home

5. quiet   loud   noisy

Synonyms

Week Nine

3

Name _____

Synonyms are words that have the same meaning.

**Match the words that have the same meanings.
Draw a line between each pair.**

1. look   rock

2. right   happy

3. stone   correct

4. pretty   see

5. glad   beautiful

Synonyms

Week Nine

4

Name _____

Synonyms are words that have the same meaning.

**Choose a word from the box that has the same meaning.
Write it on the line.**

| automobile | small | hat | boat | work |

1. ship _____

2. job _____

3. cap _____

4. little _____

5. car _____

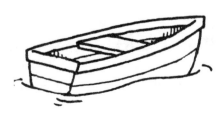

Synonyms

Week Nine

Name

Synonyms are words that have the same meaning.

Circle the words that have the same meaning.

1. like   hear   listen

2. huge   giant   strong

3. bug   insect   dog

4. talk   play   speak

5. gift   friend   present

Synonyms

Week Nine Review

Name

Match the words that have the same meanings.
Draw a line between each pair.

1. fast   noisy

2. talk   quick

3. automobile   speak

4. loud   correct

5. right   car

Compound Words

Week Ten

1

Name

A compound word combines two words to make one. **Something** is made from the words **some** and **thing**.

Circle a compound word in each sentence.

1. Have you ever looked for treasures underground?
2. You might find a Native American arrowhead or bead.
3. In some areas, you might find a horseshoe or a medicine bottle.
4. Who else might have left something behind?
5. Cowboys might have lost buttons, buckles, or coins.

Compound Words

Week Ten

2

Name

A compound word combines two words to make one. **Something** is made from the words **some** and **thing**.

Write a compound word. Then use it in a sentence.

1. back + yard _____

   _____

2. break + fast _____

   _____

3. may + be _____

   _____

4. with + out _____

   _____

Compound Words

Week Ten

3

Name _____

A compound word combines two words to make one. *Something* is made from the words *some* and *thing*.

**Match two words that can form a compound word.
Write the word on the line.**

1.	grand	brush	_____
2.	ship	body	_____
3.	paint	lace	_____
4.	no	wreck	_____
5.	shoe	mother	_____

Compound Words

Week Ten

4

Name _____

A compound word combines two words to make one. *Something* is made from the words *some* and *thing*.

Circle the compound word in each sentence.

1. Every butterfly has four wings.

2. Do you understand how insects grow and change?

3. You might see many different bugs outside your school.

4. Caterpillars do not have good eyesight.

5. Anyone can watch them use their feelers to find food.

Compound Words

Week Ten

5

Name _____

A compound word combines two words to make one. *Something* is made from the words *some* and *thing.*

Write a compound word. Then use it in a sentence.

1. skate + board _____

_____

2. every + body _____

_____

3. high + way _____

_____

4. book + case _____

_____

Compound Words

Week Ten Review

Name _____

Find the mistakes. Write each sentence correctly on the line.

1. The researchers found some thing interesting.

_____

2. The coin was buried under ground.

_____

3. May be it is more than 100 years old.

_____

4. They believe it came from a ship wreck.

_____

5. No body knows how it got from the ocean to land.

Verbs

Week Eleven

1

Name

A verb is a word that describes an action. *Run, jump,* **and** *fly* **are verbs.**

Circle each verb.

1. blue   swim

2. baseball   throw

3. wiggle   worm

4. friend   play

5. read   book

Verbs

Week Eleven

2

Name

A verb is a word that describes an action. *Run, jump,* **and** *fly* **are verbs.**

Circle the verb in each sentence.

1. Heavy rain pounds on the roof.

2. Thunder roars in the distance.

3. Lightning strikes a tall tree.

4. The storm stops suddenly.

5. The neighbors clean their street together.

Verbs

Week Eleven

3

Name _____

A verb is a word that describes an action. *Run, jump,* and *fly* are verbs.

Is the word a verb? Write *Yes* or *No* on the line.

_____ 1. eat

_____ 2. food

_____ 3. grow

_____ 4. choose

_____ 5. think

Verbs

Week Eleven

4

Name _____

A verb is a word that describes an action. *Run, jump,* and *fly* are verbs.

Circle the verb in each sentence.

1. A submarine travels underwater.

2. Boats float on the water.

3. A hovercraft rides above the water.

4. Helicopters fly in the air.

5. Trains move on tracks on the ground.

Verbs

Week Eleven

5

Name

A verb is a word that describes an action. *Run, jump,* and *fly* are verbs.

Circle the verbs.

1.	hop	bunny	jump
2.	house	make	build
3.	see	hear	taste
4.	crawl	baby	walk
5.	talk	speak	cry

Verbs

Week Eleven Review

Name

Circle the verb or verbs in each sentence.

1. Some robots walk and talk.

2. Other robots crawl like babies.

3. One robot stops at walls and spins.

4. Most robots do not grow.

5. Scientists build new robots every year.

Spelling (Long a)

Week Twelve

1

Name

There are many ways to spell the long *a* sound.

Circle the correct spelling.

1.	cake	caik
2.	snak	snake
3.	layk	lake
4.	mistake	mistayk
5.	awak	awake

Spelling (Long a)

Week Twelve

2

Name

There are many ways to spell the long *a* sound.

Arrange the letters to spell a word.

1. A Y S   _____ _____ _____

2. W A Y A   _____ _____ _____ _____

3. A L P Y   _____ _____ _____ _____

4. P A S Y R   _____ _____ _____ _____ _____

5. Y T D A O   _____ _____ _____ _____ _____

Spelling (Long a)

Week Twelve

3

Name

There are many ways to spell the long *a* sound.

Circle each word that is NOT spelled correctly. Write the correct spelling on the line.

1. A scale tells you how much something ways.

   _____

2. A ruler is a grate tool for measuring inches.

   _____

3. A tayp measure can help you measure feet and yards.

   _____

4. There are ayt ounces in a cup.

   _____

Spelling (Long a)

Week Twelve

4

Name

There are many ways to spell the long *a* sound.

Circle each word that is NOT spelled correctly. Write the correct spelling on the line.

1. rain   brane   _____

2. trane   drain   _____

3. tail   fale   _____

4. pail   traid   _____

5. dait   plate   _____

Spelling (Long a)

Week Twelve

5

Name

There are many ways to spell the long *a* sound.

Circle each word that is NOT spelled correctly. Write the correct spelling on the line.

1. Visit a dentist if you feel payn in a tooth.

   _____

2. Try not to arrive too lait.

   _____

3. You will have to wate your turn.

   _____

4. Remember to brush your teeth every daye.

   _____

Spelling (Long a)

Week Twelve Review

Name

Find the mistake in each sentence.
Then write each sentence correctly on the line.

1. Baseball is a grate game.

   _____

2. A baseball ways about five ounces.

   _____

3. You need nine players to maik a team.

   _____

4. Players add taip to the bat to get a better grip.

   _____

Monthly Review

Name _____

A. Find the mistakes. Then write each sentence correctly on the line.

1. Do you under stand why break fast is important?

   _____

2. It gives you energy that lasts all daye long.

   _____

3. Choose some thing healthy and tasty.

   _____

4. Your body and brane get energy from your food.

   _____

5. No body should skip this grait meal.

   _____

B. Find five verbs. Go across and down. Write them on the lines.

S	T	A	R	T
L	H	G	P	A
C	R	A	W	L
M	O	N	Y	K
S	W	I	M	G

_____

_____

_____

_____

C. Choose a word from the box to complete each sentence.

See   stone   Maybe   huge   glad

1. *Happy* has the same meaning as _____.
2. _____ is a compound word.
3. *Rock* has the same meaning as _____.
4. _____ is a verb.
5. *Giant* has the same meaning as _____.

Capitalization

Week Thirteen

1

Name

A proper noun names a specific person, place, or thing. Capitalize all proper nouns. *Abraham Lincoln, California,* and *Brooklyn Bridge* are proper nouns.

Circle the word that is capitalized correctly.

1.   mexico   Mexico
2.   Peter   peter
3.   Broadway   broadway
4.   fido   Fido
5.   san diego   San Diego

Capitalization

Week Thirteen

2

Name

A proper noun names a specific person, place, or thing. Capitalize all proper nouns. *Abraham Lincoln, California,* and *Brooklyn Bridge* are proper nouns.

Circle the word that should be capitalized.
Write the word correctly on the line.

1. Clara barton was a famous nurse. _____

2. She was born in massachusetts. _____

3. She founded the American red Cross. _____

4. Barton also set up an early free
public school in new Jersey. _____

5. Her home in maryland is a museum._____

Capitalization

Week Thirteen

3

Name _____

A proper noun names a specific person, place, or thing. Capitalize all proper nouns. *Abraham Lincoln, California,* and *Brooklyn Bridge* are proper nouns.

Choose the correct word. Write it on the line.

1. George _____ (washington, Washington) was the first president.
2. A _____ (President, president) is the head of a country.
3. The White _____ (House, house) was completed in 1800.
4. Do you know what _____ (road, Road) the building is on?

Short Vowels

Week Thirteen

4

Name _____

A proper noun names a specific person, place, or thing. Capitalize all proper nouns. *Abraham Lincoln, California,* and *Brooklyn Bridge* are proper nouns.

Circle the word or words that are capitalized correctly.

1. teacher   mr. lynch
2. State   Ohio
3. Water   Lake Huron
4. dallas   city
5. Place   France

Capitalization

Week Thirteen

5

Name

A proper noun names a specific person, place, or thing. Capitalize all proper nouns. *Abraham Lincoln, California,* and *Brooklyn Bridge* are proper nouns.

Circle the word needs a capital letter. Write the word correctly on the line.

1. Jackie robinson played baseball. _____

2. He was born in georgia. _____

3. Later, his family moved to california. _____

4. He joined the Brooklyn dodgers in 1947. _____

5. He was the first African American player on this
   new York team. _____

Capitalization

Week Thirteen Review

Name

Find the mistakes. Write each sentence correctly on the line.

1. The mississippi River is a very long River.

   _____

2. It is the second longest in the united states.

   _____

3. It flows from minnesota to the gulf of mexico.

   _____

4. The longest u.s. river is the missouri River.

   _____

5. Both of These rivers are in north america.

   _____

Subject-Verb Agreement

Week Fourteen

1

Name

A singular subject names one thing. Use a singular verb. *(The girl hops.)*
A plural subject names more than one. Use a plural verb. *(The boys jump.)*

Choose the correct word. Write it on the line.

1. Some birds _____ (fly, flies) in flocks.

2. A bird _____ (fly, flies) in the air.

3. Some animals _____ (live, lives) underwater.

4. A lobster _____ (live, lives) underwater.

5. Some turtles _____ (live, lives) on land or water.

Subject-Verb Agreement

Week Fourteen

2

Name

A singular subject names one thing. Use a singular verb. *(The girl hops.)*
A plural subject names more than one. Use a plural verb. *(The boys jump.)*

**Choose a word from the box to complete each sentence.
Write it on the line.**

help	helps	rings	sits	take

1. Computers _____ at the office.

2. The worker _____ on a chair.

3. The telephone _____ .

4. A calculator _____ you add.

5. People _____ the train to work.

Subject-Verb Agreement

Week Fourteen

3

A singular subject names one thing. Use a singular verb. *(The girl hops.)*
A plural subject names more than one. Use a plural verb. *(The boys jump.)*

Choose the correct word. Write it on the line.

1. A whale _____ (is, are) a mammal.

2. Sharks _____ (is, are) fish.

3. An ant _____ (is, are) an insect.

4. A snake _____ (is, are) a reptile.

5. Penguins _____ (is, are) birds.

Subject-Verb Agreement

Week Fourteen

4

A singular subject names one thing. Use a singular verb. *(The girl hops.)*
A plural subject names more than one. Use a plural verb. *(The boys jump.)*

Write the correct verb on the line.

1. A strong wind blow from the north. _____

2. Dark clouds moves very quickly. _____

3. Heavy winds blows for many hours. _____

4. At last, the storm stop. _____

5. The sun shine. _____

Subject-Verb Agreement

Week Fourteen

5

Name _____

A singular subject names one thing. Use a singular verb. *(The girl hops.)*
A plural subject names more than one. Use a plural verb. *(The boys jump.)*

Choose the correct word. Write it on the line.

1. A book _____ a cover.
   (has, have)

2. Newspapers _____ a front page.
   (has, have)

3. Letters _____ an address.
   (has, have)

4. The speech _____ an important message.
   (has, have)

Subject-Verb Agreement

Week Fourteen Review

Name _____

Find the mistakes. Write each sentence correctly on the line.

1. Stars shines in the night sky.

   _____

2. The moon look full tonight.

   _____

3. Saturn have a huge ring.

   _____

4. The planets is very far away.

   _____

5. The sun rise in the morning.

   _____

Complete Sentences

Week Fifteen

1

Name

A complete sentence has a subject and a verb.

Is the sentence complete? Write *Yes* or *No* on the line.

_____ 1. Some dolphins help the U.S. Navy.

_____ 2. They find unsafe objects.

_____ 3. In the water.

_____ 4. Dolphins use sound to find things.

_____ 5. Friendly animals.

Complete Sentences

Week Fifteen

2

Name

A complete sentence has a subject and a verb.

**Match the parts to create complete sentences.
Draw a line between parts that fit together.**

1. Bees   honey.

2. The queen bee lays   eggs.

3. Some bees make   fuzzy.

4. A female honeybee   live in hives.

5. Bees are   dies when it stings.

Complete Sentences

Week Fifteen

3

Name _____

A complete sentence has a subject and a verb.

Is the sentence complete? Write _Yes_ or _No_ on the line.

_____ 1. Machines are everywhere.

_____ 2. We use them.

_____ 3. To play and to work.

_____ 4. Drive cars.

_____ 5. A really big wheel.

Complete Sentences

Week Fifteen

4

Name _____

A complete sentence has a subject and a verb.

Complete each sentence.

1. A camera _____.

2. _____ sings.

3. The painter_____.

4. _____ rings.

5. The Earth _____.

Complete Sentences

Week Fifteen

5

Name _____

A complete sentence has a subject and a verb.

Is the sentence complete? Write *Yes* or *No* on the line.

_____ 1. Paul, the firefighter.

_____ 2. Lives in Connecticut.

_____ 3. To put out fires.

_____ 4. A bright red fire engine.

_____ 5. The flames rise higher.

Complete Sentences

Week Fifteen Review

Name _____

Find the mistakes. Write each sentence correctly on the line.

1. The Pilgrims. Celebrated the first Thanksgiving.

_____

2. We eat. A big meal.

_____

3. Some people. Like to watch a colorful parade.

_____

4. Football players. Appear on television.

_____

5. Families around the country. Share their food.

_____

Spelling
(Long e and i)

Week Sixteen

1

Name

There are many ways to spell the long *e* sound.

Circle the correct spelling.

1.   green   grean

2.   meen   mean

3.   thri   three

4.   deap   deep

5.   ice cream   ice creem

Spelling
(Long e and i)

Week Sixteen

2

Name

There are many ways to spell the long *i* sound.

Arrange the letters to spell a word with the long *i* sound.

1. W Y H   ___ ___ ___

2. E I K L   ___ ___ ___ ___

3. I G H H   ___ ___ ___ ___

4. E Z I S   ___ ___ ___ ___

5. G I T H M   ___ ___ ___ ___ ___

Spelling
(Long e and i)

Week Sixteen

Name

There are many ways to spell the long *e* and *i* sounds.
Circle each word that is NOT spelled correctly.

Write the correct spelling on the line.

1. Some animals sleap during the day. _____

2. Other animals rest at nite. _____

3. Scientists think that some animals dreem,
   too. _____

4. Frogs do not nead to sleep at all. _____

5. What tyme do you wake up each day? _____

Spelling
(Long e and i)

Week Sixteen

Name

There are many ways to spell the long *e* and *i* sounds.

Circle the correct spelling.

1.   pie   py

2.   eyes   eiz

3.   leef   leaf

4.   feel   feal

5.   brite   bright

Spelling (Long e and i)

Week Sixteen

5

Name

There are many ways to spell the long *e* and *i* sounds.

Circle each word that is NOT spelled correctly. Write the correct spelling on the line.

1. A lyme is a small round fruit. _____

2. It grows on treas. _____

3. When it is rype, the skin is green. _____

4. If you squeaze this fruit, you get juice. _____

5. The peal is very bitter. _____

Spelling (Long e and i)

Week Sixteen Review

Name

Find the mistakes. Write each sentence correctly on the line.

1. Whi do we have eyz?

   _____

2. They help you sea the world around you.

   _____

3. Your syte is stronger during the day than at nyte.

   _____

4. Some people nead glasses to see things far away.

   _____

5. Other people use glasses to reed books and magazines.

   _____

Monthly Review

Name

A. Find the mistakes.
Write each sentence correctly on the line.

1. New york city is the largest City in the united states.

   _____

2. About eight million People. Lives there.

   _____

3. At nite. Lytes shines in Times Square.

   _____

4. The empire state building have 102 stories.

   _____

5. Central park is a huge grean space. In the middle of the city.

   _____

B. Write the answers in the puzzle.

Across

1 it has roots and bark
3 opposite of low
5 it falls in autumn
8 you do it at night

Down

2 opposite of left
4 yellow and blue combined
6 what your fingers do
7 what a clock tells

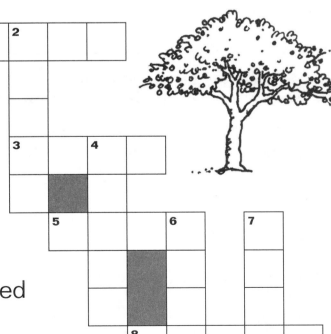

Possessive Nouns

Week Seventeen
1

Name

A possessive noun shows ownership. The *boy's* umbrella flew away in the wind. Possessive nouns use apostrophes.

Match the phrases with the same meaning.

_____ 1. the petals of the flower   A. the wind's roar

_____ 2. the leaves of the tree   B. the bee's buzz

_____ 3. the song of the bird   C. the bird's song

_____ 4. the roar of the wind   D. the flower's petals

_____ 5. the buzz of the bee   E. the tree's leaves

Possessive Nouns

Week Seventeen
2

Name

A possessive noun shows ownership. The *boy's* umbrella flew away in the wind. Possessive nouns use apostrophes.

Each phrase is missing an apostrophe (').
Write the correct phrase on the line.

1. a books cover   _____

2. a chairs leg   _____

3. a teachers class _____

4. a pencils point   _____

5. a friends smile   _____

Possessive Nouns

Week Seventeen 3

Name

A possessive noun shows ownership. The *boy's* umbrella flew away in the wind. Possessive nouns use apostrophes.

Circle each word that is missing an apostrophe (').
Write the correct word on the line.

1. Did you see the turtles egg? _____

2. It is in the museums collection. _____

3. The eggs shell is very thin. _____

4. Janes story is about turtles. _____

5. The storys ending is very exciting. _____

Possessive Nouns

Week Seventeen 4

Name

A possessive noun shows ownership. The *boy's* umbrella flew away in the wind. Possessive nouns use apostrophes.

Each phrase is missing an apostrophe (').
Write the correct phrase on the line.

1. a volcanos lava _____

2. a cliffs edge _____

3. a mountains peak _____

4. a rivers current _____

5. a waterfalls roar _____

Possessive Nouns

Week Seventeen 5

A possessive noun shows ownership. The *boy's* umbrella
flew away in the wind. Possessive nouns use apostrophes.

Circle each word that is missing an apostrophe (').
Write the correct word on the line.

1. Japans largest city is Tokyo.

   _____

2. Tokyos streets are often busy.

   _____

3. The citys signs and lights are famous.

   _____

4. Every day, people use the subways 1,000 stations.

   _____

Possessive Nouns

Week Seventeen Review

Find the mistakes. Write each sentence correctly.

1. The scientist heard a loud birds quack.

   _____

2. She found an egg near the ponds edge.

   _____

3. The eggs shell was spotted brown and white.

   _____

4. A ducks feathers are waterproof.

   _____

5. A swans feathers are usually black or white.

   _____

Verb Forms (Adding –ing)

Name

Week Eighteen 1

You can add *–ing* to many verbs. The new word tells an action that is happening.

Add *–ing* to each verb. Write the new verb on the line.

1. talk + *–ing* _____

2. find + *–ing* _____

3. think + *–ing* _____

4. teach + *–ing* _____

5. wander + *–ing* _____

Verb Forms (Adding –ing)

Name

Week Eighteen 2

You can add *–ing* to many verbs. The new word tells an action that is happening.

Add *–ing* to the verb to complete each sentence. Write it on the line.

1. A tower is _____ (lean) in Pisa, Italy.

2. It is _____ (fall) a little bit every year.

3. The tower has been _____ (stand) for more than 800 years.

4. People enjoy _____ (look) at the strange tower.

5. Experts are _____ (discuss) ways to keep the tower from tipping over.

Verb Forms (Adding *–ing*)

Week Eighteen

3

Name

To add *–ing* to a verb that ends in e, first drop the *e.* Then add *–ing.*

Add *–ing* to each verb.

1. bake + *–ing* _____

2. hike + *–ing* _____

3. smile + *–ing* _____

4. wiggle + *–ing* _____

5. prepare + *–ing* _____

Verb Forms (Adding *–ing*)

Week Eighteen

4

Name

To add *–ing* to a verb that ends in e, first drop the *e.* Then add *–ing.*

Add *–ing* to the verb to complete each sentence.

1. Cars are _____ (race) around the track.

2. The race is _____ (take) place in Indianapolis.

3. Every driver is _____ (hope) to win the race.

4. One team is _____ (change) a tire.

5. The reporters are _____ (announce) the winner.

Verb Forms (Adding *-ing*)

Week Eighteen

5

Name

Sometimes you need to double the final letter when adding *-ing* to a verb.

Add *-ing* to each verb. Write the new verb on the line.

1. win + *-ing*   _____

2. stop + *-ing*   _____

3. swim + *-ing*   _____

4. knit + *-ing*   _____

5. rub + *-ing*   _____

Verb Forms (Adding *-ing*)

Week Eighteen Review

Name

Find the mistakes. Write each sentence correctly.

1. The director is makeing a new movie.

_____

2. She is tellng the actors where to move.

_____

3. The actors are listeng carefully.

_____

4. People are stoping to watch the crew.

_____

5. Soon, the audience is claping very loudly.

_____

Alphabetical Order

Week Nineteen 1

Name

Alphabetical order is the same as ABC order. Words that begin with *a* come before words that begin with *b,* and so on.

Write the words in alphabetical order on the lines.

knight   moat   castle   queen   armor

1. _____

2. _____

3. _____

4. _____

5. _____

Alphabetical Order

Week Nineteen 2

Name

Alphabetical order is the same as ABC order. Words that begin with *a* come before words that begin with *b,* and so on.

Are the words in alphabetical order? Write *Yes* or *No* on the lines.

_____ 1. avenue   road   street

_____ 2. book   newspaper   magazine

_____ 3. boxer   retriever   poodle

_____ 4. view   wait   young

_____ 5. family   friend   game

Alphabetical Order

Week Nineteen 3

Name

Alphabetical order is the same as ABC order. Words that begin with *a* come before words that begin with *b,* and so on.

Write the words in alphabetical order on the lines.

sunflower violet tulip rose poppy

1. _____

2. _____

3. _____

4. _____

5. _____

© Weekly Reader Corp.

Alphabetical Order

Week Nineteen 4

Name

Alphabetical order is the same as ABC order. Words that begin with *a* come before words that begin with *b,* and so on.

Choose a word from the box that fits the alphabetical order. Write it on the line.

emerald opal silver copper topaz

1. moonstone, _____, pearl

2. ruby, _____, tin

3. diamond, _____, gold

4. tin, _____, zinc

5. bronze, _____, diamond

© Weekly Reader Corp.

Alphabetical Order

Week Nineteen

5

Name

Alphabetical order is the same as ABC order. Words that begin with *a* come before words that begin with *b,* and so on. If the first letters are the same, look at the second letters.

Write the words in alphabetical order on the lines.

lion   tiger   leopard   jaguar   lynx

1. _____
2. _____
3. _____
4. _____
5. _____

ZOO

Alphabetical Order

Week Nineteen Review

Name

Write the words in alphabetical order on the lines.

1. fish, bird, snake

_____

2. purple, green, yellow, orange, blue, red

_____

3. pencil, poem, paper

_____

4. Mercury, Venus, Earth, Mars, Jupiter, Saturn, Uranus, Neptune, Pluto

_____

Spelling
(Long *o* and *u*)

Name

Week Twenty

1

There are many ways to spell the long *o* sound.

Circle the correct spelling.

1. hoam   home
2. coat   cote
3. botes   boats
4. float   flote
5. throw   thro

Spelling
(Long *o* and *u*)

Name

Week Twenty

2

There are many ways to spell the long *u* sound.

Arrange the letters to spell a word with the long *u* sound.

1. O N M O   __ __ __ __
2. D U R E   __ __ __ __
3. R O B M O   __ __ __ __ __
4. H W T R E   __ __ __ __ __
5. P O N O S   __ __ __ __ __

Spelling
(Long *o* and *u*)

Week Twenty
3

Name

There are many ways to spell the long *o* and *u* sounds.

Circle each word that is NOT spelled correctly.
Write the correct spelling on the line.

1. The musicians play a happy toon.

   _____

2. Their noats are loud and clear.

   _____

3. The groop includes many instruments.

   _____

4. To play a tuba, you need to bloe hard.

   _____

Spelling
(Long *o* and *u*)

Week Twenty
4

Name

There are many ways to spell the long *o* and *u* sounds.

Circle the correct spelling.

1.   know   knowe

2.   toe   towe

3.   soop   soup

4.   room   rume

5.   few   fyu

Spelling
(Long *o* and *u*)

Week Twenty

Name

There are many ways to spell the long *o* and *u* sounds.

Circle each word that is NOT spelled correctly.
Write the correct spelling on the line.

1. Many modern rodes have two layers.

_____

2. Belowe the concrete is a layer of hard soil or gravel.

_____

3. The lower layer helps two support the road.

_____

4. Did yoo know that the top of most roads is slightly curved?

_____

Spelling
(Long *o* and *u*)

Week Twenty Review

Name

Find the mistakes. Write each sentence correctly on the line.

1. In spring, many flowers begin to groe.

_____

2. Summer begins in Joon each year.

_____

3. A bloo moon happens when there are to full moons in one month.

_____

4. In fall, winds bloe and leaves flote down.

_____

Monthly Review

Name

A. Find the mistakes. Write each sentence correctly on the line.

1. A student is writeing about famous peoples houses.

   _____

2. She is keepng noats about what she reads.

   _____

3. She is planing to write about a presidents childhood.

   _____

4. Abraham Lincolns first hoam was in Kentucky.

   _____

5. It was a log cabin that had only one rume.

   _____

B. Write the animals in alphabetical order, A to Z. The circled letters will answer the riddle.

(plover   turtle   falcon   spider   locust   mongoose   elephant   cobra   gecko)

___ ___ ⬭ ___ ___

___ ___ ___ ___ ___ ⬭ ___ ___

___ ___ ___ ⬭ ___ ___

___ ___ ___ ⬭ ___ ___ ___

___ ___ ⬭ ___ ___ ___

___ ___ ___ ⬭ ___ ___ ___

___ ___ ___ ⬭ ___ ___ ___

___ ___ ___ ⬭ ___ ___

___ ___ ⬭ ___ ___ ___ ___

What comes after Z in the dictionary?

The ⬭⬭⬭⬭   ⬭⬭⬭⬭⬭

Antonyms

Week Twenty-One

1

Name

Antonyms are words that have opposite meanings.
Do the words have opposite meanings?

Write *Yes* or *No* on the lines.

_____	1.	happy	sad
_____	2.	old	young
_____	3.	smart	wise
_____	4.	wet	dry
_____	5.	mean	nice

Antonyms

Week Twenty-One

2

Name

Antonyms are words that have opposite meanings.
Match each word with its opposite.

Draw a line between each pair of antonyms.

1.	long	dirty
2.	easy	outside
3.	thick	short
4.	inside	thin
5.	clean	hard

Antonyms

Week Twenty-One

3

Name _____

Antonyms are words that have opposite meanings.

Write the word from the box with the opposite meaning on the line.

| sour | small | soft | sloppy | start |

1. large _____

2. stop _____

3. hard _____

4. neat _____

5. sweet _____

Antonyms

Week Twenty-One

4

Name _____

Antonyms are words that have opposite meanings. Look at the underlined word.

Write a word that has the opposite meaning on the line.

1. The building is very <u>tall</u>.

   _____

2. The playground will be <u>expensive</u> to build.

   _____

3. The town's park is next to the <u>old</u> library.

   _____

4. One street sign has large <u>black</u> letters.

   _____

Antonyms

Week Twenty-One

Name

Antonyms are words that have opposite meanings.
Match each word with its opposite.

Draw a line between antonyms.

1. fast   full
2. asleep   interesting
3. empty   below
4. dull   slow
5. above   awake

Antonyms

Week Twenty-One Review

Name

Circle the words that have opposite meanings.

1. short   long   big
2. empty   near   full
3. hurry   stop   start
4. inside   below   above
5. fresh   free   stale

Contractions

Week Twenty-Two

1

Name

Contractions are shortened words that combine two words. *Are* and *not* are combined in the contraction *aren't*. Contractions include apostrophes.

Circle each contraction.

1. It isn't true that lightning never strikes the same place twice.
2. You'll find that some tall buildings are often hit by lightning.
3. During a storm, you'd be smart to stay away from tall trees.
4. Lakes and rivers aren't safe during a storm.
5. I'm very interested in weather.

Contractions

Week Twenty-Two

2

Name

Contractions are shortened words that combine two words. *Are* and *not* are combined in the contraction *aren't*. Contractions include apostrophes.

Write the contraction for each pair of words on the line.

1. could + not _____

2. can + not _____

3. is + not _____

4. are + not _____

5. will + not _____

Contractions

Week Twenty-Two

3

Name _____

Contractions are shortened words that combine two words. *Are* and *not* are combined in the contraction *aren't.* Contractions include apostrophes.

Write the two words that form the contraction on the lines.

1. doesn't _____ + _____

2. you're _____ + _____

3. she'll _____ + _____

4. didn't _____ + _____

5. he's _____ + _____

Contractions

Week Twenty-Two

4

Name _____

Contractions are shortened words that combine two words. *Are* and *not* are combined in the contraction *aren't.* Contractions include apostrophes.

Complete each sentence with a contraction.

1. The reporter _____ (did, not) see the accident.
2. _____ (She, is) going to ask what happened.
3. The article _____ (will, not) be difficult to write.
4. The editor says _____ (it, is) going to be on the front page.
5. _____ (He, will) make sure there are no mistakes.

Contractions

Week Twenty-Two

5

Name

Contractions are shortened words that combine two words. *Are* and *not* are combined in the contraction *aren't.* Contractions include apostrophes.

Write the contraction for each pair of words on the line.

1. I + am _____

2. she + is _____

3. they + are _____

4. we + will _____

5. would + not _____

Contractions

Week Twenty-Two Review

Name

Find the mistakes. Write each sentence correctly on the line.

1. We'ill go to the museum tomorrow.

_____

2. It isnt very far away.

_____

3. The tour wo'nt take more than one hour.

_____

4. Arent you looking forward to the trip?

_____

Verb Forms (Adding *-ed*)

Week Twenty-Three

1

Name

You can add *-ed* to many verbs to show what already happened.

Add *-ed* to each verb.
Write the new verb on the line.

1. walk   +   *-ed*   _____

2. play   +   *-ed*   _____

3. laugh   +   *-ed*   _____

4. visit   +   *-ed*   _____

5. collect +   *-ed*   _____

Verb Forms (Adding *-ed*)

Week Twenty-Three

2

Name

You can add *-ed* to many verbs to show what already happened.

Add *-ed* to the verb to complete each sentence.

1. Thomas Edison _____ (invent) many things.

2. He _____ (start) his work in New Jersey.

3. Many people _____ (listen) to his early
   sound recordings.

4. His ideas _____ (help) make lightbulbs popular.

5. Edison _____ (learn) by doing experiments.

Verb Forms (Adding –ed)

Week Twenty-Three

3

Name

To add *–ed* to a verb that ends in *e*, add only *–d*. To add *–ed* to a verb that ends in *y*, change the *y* to *i* and add *–ed*.

Add *–ed* to each verb. Write the new verb on the line.

1. like   +   *–ed*   _____

2. study   +   *–ed*   _____

3. save   +   *–ed*   _____

4. carry   +   *–ed*   _____

5. copy   +   *–ed*   _____

Verb Forms (Adding *–ed*)

Week Twenty-Three

4

Name

To add *–ed* to a verb that ends in *e*, add only *–d*. To add *–ed* to a verb that ends in *y*, change the *y* to *i* and add *–ed*.

Add *–ed* to the verb to complete each sentence.

1. Franklin and Eleanor Roosevelt _____ (marry) in 1905.

2. They _____ (live) in the White House for 12 years.

3. Franklin D. Roosevelt was _____ (nickname) FDR.

4. He _____ (try) to find ways to help people find jobs.

Verb Forms (Adding *-ed*)

Week Twenty-Three

5

Name

Sometimes you need to double the final letter before adding *-ed* to a verb.

Add *-ed* to each verb.
Write the new verb on the line.

1. stop + *-ed* _____

2. hurry + *-ed* _____

3. stir + *-ed* _____

4. plan + *-ed* _____

5. worry + *-ed* _____

Verb Forms (Adding *-ed*)

Week Twenty-Three Review

Name

Find the mistakes. Write each sentence correctly on the line.

1. A streetcar was traped under a heavy snowfall.

   _____

2. The riders worryed about what would happen.

   _____

3. The rescue team hurryed to the scene.

   _____

4. They arriveed minutes later.

   _____

Spelling
(R-Controlled Vowels)

Week Twenty-Four

1

Name

Words with _r_ follow many spelling patterns.

Circle the correct spelling.

1.   swimmar   swimmer

2.   countir   counter

3.   player   playur

4.   nicer   nicir

5.   rulur   ruler

Spelling
(R-Controlled Vowels)

Week Twenty-Four

2

Name

Words with _r_ follow many spelling patterns.

Arrange the letters to spell a word.

1. R O F M   ___ ___ ___ ___

2. R U O P   ___ ___ ___ ___

3. O S H E R   ___ ___ ___ ___ ___

4. D B A O R   ___ ___ ___ ___ ___

5. L O R O F   ___ ___ ___ ___ ___

Spelling
(R-Controlled Vowels)

Week Twenty-Four

3

Name

Words with _r_ follow many spelling patterns.

Circle each word that is NOT spelled correctly.
Write the correct spelling on the line.

1. The weathir will change tomorrow.

   _____

2. We will probably get a lot moar snow.

   _____

3. Some stors might be closed because of the storm.

   _____

4. It will not be warme enough for rain.

   _____

Spelling
(R-Controlled Vowels)

Week Twenty-Four

4

Name

Words with _r_ follow many spelling patterns.

Circle the correct spelling.

1.   bird   burd

2.   dollir   dollar

3.   feathur   feather

4.   earth   erth

5.   motor   moter

Spelling
(R-Controlled Vowels)

Week Twenty-Four

5

Name

Words with _r_ follow many spelling patterns.

Circle each word that is NOT spelled correctly.
Write the correct spelling on the line.

1. The boys and gurls visited the city hall.

   _____

2. Furst they talked about the law.

   _____

3. Then they visited a real cort.

   _____

4. A lawyur talked about his job.

   _____

Spelling
(R-Controlled Vowels)

Week Twenty-Four Review

Name

Find the mistakes. Write the corrected sentences on the lines.

1. The gurl makes a beautiful new skurt.

   _____

2. She puts the fabric on the flore.

   _____

3. Hur brothir helps a little, too.

   _____

4. He holds the rulir while she cuts the cloth.

   _____

5. Sometimes four hands are bettar than two.

   _____

Monthly Review

Name _____

A. Find the mistakes. Write each sentence correctly on the line.

1. Helen Keller could'nt see or heer.

_____

2. Helen's family liveed in Alabama.

_____

3. At furst, they did'nt think Helen would evir communicate.

_____

4. Then Anne Sullivan helpd her lurn.

_____

5. The two friends traveld together for many yeers.

_____

**B. Circle five pairs of opposites. Go across and down.
Write the pairs on the lines.**

T	R	F	O	S	I	T
S	M	A	L	L	S	B
U	C	S	A	O	T	E
H	O	T	R	W	A	G
W	L	S	G	P	N	I
I	D	O	E	N	D	N

_____ and _____

_____ and _____

_____ and _____

_____ and _____

_____ and _____

C. Complete the words. Write *a, e, i, o,* or *u* on the blank lines.

D O L L ___ R

T H U N D ___ R

G ___ R L

W ___ R L D

N ___ R S E

Capitalization

Week Twenty-Five

1

Name _____

A proper noun names a specific person, place, or thing. Capitalize all proper nouns. *Abraham Lincoln, California,* and *Brooklyn Bridge* are proper nouns.

Circle the noun that is capitalized correctly.

1.   mrs. Chen   Mrs. Chen

2.   new Mexico   New Mexico

3.   Mount everest   Mount Everest

4.   Lake Erie   lake Erie

5.   Fifth Avenue   Fifth avenue

Capitalization

Week Twenty-Five

2

Name _____

A proper noun names a specific person, place, or thing. *Abraham Lincoln, California,* and *Brooklyn Bridge* are proper nouns. Capitalize all proper nouns and the first letter in every sentence.

Choose the correct word.

1. Wilma _____ (Rudolph, rudolph) is one of my heroes.

2. She won _____ (four, Four) gold medals in the Olympics.

3. _____(later, Later) she became a teacher and a coach in Tennessee.

4. In 2004, the United _____ (states, States) Post Office put her face on a stamp.

Capitalization

Week Twenty-Five

3

Name

A proper noun names a specific person, place, or thing. *Abraham Lincoln, California,* and *Brooklyn Bridge* are proper nouns. Capitalize all proper nouns and the first letter in every sentence.

Circle the word that should be capitalized. Write it correctly on the line.

1. Do you think it rains more in march or in July?

_____

2. Is Los angeles or Boston closer to your house?

_____

3. where would you find the Smithsonian Institution?

_____

4. Are there more people living in North dakota or Wyoming?

_____

Capitalization

Week Twenty-Five

4

Name

A proper noun names a specific person, place, or thing. Capitalize all proper nouns. *Abraham Lincoln, California,* and *Brooklyn Bridge* are proper nouns.

Circle the noun that is capitalized correctly.

1.	fort Knox	Fort Knox
2.	Pacific Ocean	pacific Ocean
3.	john Smith	John Smith
4.	King Tut	king tut
5.	south Carolina	South Carolina

Capitalization

Week Twenty-Five

5

Name

A proper noun names a specific person, place, or thing. *Abraham Lincoln,* *California,* and *Brooklyn Bridge* are proper nouns. Capitalize all proper nouns and the first letter in every sentence.

Circle the word that should be capitalized. Write it correctly on the line.

1. At home i like to read stories about knights.

   _____

2. Some of my favorite tales are about King arthur.

   _____

3. He lived in Great britain during the Middle Ages.

   _____

4. brave knights fought against monsters and evil.

   _____

Capitalization

Week Twenty-Five Review

Name

Find the mistakes. Write each sentence correctly on the line.

1. four presidents' faces are Carved into mount Rushmore.

   _____

2. On the left, you can see George washington.

   _____

3. on the right, you will find theodore roosevelt.

   _____

4. This Famous Mountain is near keystone, south Dakota.

   _____

Subject-Verb Agreement

Week Twenty-Six

1

Name

A singular subject names one thing. Use a singular verb. *(The girl hops.)*
A plural subject names more than one. Use a plural verb. *(The boys jump.)*

Choose the correct word. Write it on the line.

1. Peaches _____ (grow, grows) on trees.

2. Workers _____ (pick, picks) the ripe fruits.

3. A truck _____ (carry, carries) the peaches to market.

4. A store _____ (sell, sells) the fuzzy fruits.

5. People _____ (eat, eats) them at home.

Subject-Verb Agreement

Week Twenty-Six

2

Name

A singular subject names one thing. Use a singular verb. *(The girl hops.)*
A plural subject names more than one. Use a plural verb. *(The boys jump.)*

**Choose a word from box to complete each sentence.
Write it on the line.**

> hear   sings   rings   practice   ring

1. Bells _____.

2. A bell _____.

3. Singers _____ every day.

4. I _____ a new song on the radio.

5. The singer _____ the song very softly.

Subject-Verb Agreement

Week Twenty-Six

3

Name

A singular subject names one thing. Use a singular verb. (The girl hops.)
A plural subject names more than one. Use a plural verb. (The boys jump.)

Choose the correct word. Write it on the line.

1. A nurse _____ (help, helps) other people.

2. Nurses _____ (learn, learns) many useful skills.

3. The hospital _____ (is, are) very new.

4. Hospitals _____ (is, are) very clean.

5. Cleaners _____ (try, tries) to remove germs.

Subject-Verb Agreement

Week Twenty-Six

4

Name

A singular subject names one thing. Use a singular verb. (The girl hops.)
A plural subject names more than one. Use a plural verb. (The boys jump.)

Circle each verb. Write the correct verb on the line.

1. The waves crashes on the beach.
   _____

2. A rock sink to the bottom of the lake.
   _____

3. The waterfall make a loud roar.
   _____

4. Lake Victoria are in Africa.
   _____

Subject-Verb Agreement

Week Twenty-Six

5

Name

A singular subject names one thing. Use a singular verb. *(The girl hops.)*
A plural subject names more than one. Use a plural verb. *(The boys jump.)*

Choose the correct word. Write it on the line.

1. Spiders _____ (spin, spins) webs.

2. A web _____ (catch, catches) insects.

3. A fly _____ (has, have) compound eyes.

4. Flies _____ (do, does) not live very long.

5. Centipedes _____ (has, have) many legs.

Subject-Verb Agreement

Week Twenty-Six Review

Name

Find the mistakes. Write each sentence correctly on the line.

1. Stars is very far away.

_____

2. The moon travel around Earth.

_____

3. Our galaxy have many stars and planets.

_____

4. A constellation are a group of stars.

_____

Rhyming Words

Week Twenty-Seven

1

Name

Rhyming words have the same end sounds. The sounds do not always have the same spelling. Do the words rhyme?

Write *Yes* or *No* on the line.

_____ 1. chair   bear

_____ 2. eyes   size

_____ 3. wood   food

_____ 4. lean   leap

_____ 5. four   store

Rhyming Words

Week Twenty-Seven

2

Name

Rhyming words have the same end sounds. The sounds do not always have the same spelling.

Circle the rhyming words.

1. cheer   chair   near

2. fail   real   feel

3. now   grow   toe

4. much   pouch   touch

5. laugh   tough   half

Rhyming Words

Week Twenty-Seven

3

Name

Rhyming words have the same end sounds. The sounds do not always have the same spelling.

Write a word that rhymes on each line.

1. great   st_____

2. nose   gr_____

3. plane   r_____

4. flower   h_____

5. please   b_____

Rhyming Words

Week Twenty-Seven

4

Name

Rhyming words have the same end sounds. The sounds do not always have the same spelling.

Circle the rhyming words.

1.	booth	south	truth
2.	sew	stew	know
3.	lake	leak	steak
4.	throw	new	true
5.	fuzz	was	is

Rhyming Words

Week Twenty-Seven

5

Name

Rhyming words have the same end sounds. The sounds do not always have the same spelling. Match the rhyming words.

Draw a line between each pair of words that rhyme.

1.   stare   sticks

2.   food   plate

3.   mix   noise

4.   wait   hair

5.   boys   rude

Rhyming Words

Week Twenty-Seven Review

Name

Circle the words that rhyme in each sentence.

1. Is it rude to chew food with your mouth open?

2. Please avoid the bees in the park.

3. The corner store has four windows.

4. Does he know how to sew a shirt?

5. The boys in the yard made a lot of noise.

Spelling
(Consonant Blends)

Week Twenty-Eight

1

Name

Two or more consonants can go together to spell one sound.

Write *c, k,* or *ck* on the line to complete each word.

1. blan_____et

2. for_____

3. bu_____et

4. lu_____y

5. cir_____le

Spelling
(Consonant Blends)

Week Twenty-Eight

2

Name

Two or more consonants can go together to spell one sound.

Circle the correct spelling.

1. white   wite

2. choose   shoose

3. whind   wind

4. shure   sure

5. wheel   weel

Spelling
(Consonant Blends)

Week Twenty-Eight

Name

Two or more consonants can go together to spell one sound.

Write the correct word on each line.

1. The new _____ will cross the river.
   (bridge, brige)

2. At this _____ it is not yet finished.
   (stadge, stage)

3. A worker steps close to the _____ .
   (eje, edge)

4. The best worker earns a special _____ .
   (badge, bage)

Spelling
(Consonant Blends)

Week Twenty-Eight

4

Name

Two or more consonants can go together to spell one sound.

Write *x* or *cks* to complete each word.

1. bo_____

2. blo_____

3. che_____

4. wa_____

5. sti_____

Spelling
(Consonant Blends)

Week Twenty-Eight

5

Name

Two or more consonants can go together to spell one sound.

Circle the correct spelling.

1. match   matsh

2. beash   beach

3. itsh   itch

4. bensh   bench

5. peach   peash

Spelling
(Consonant Blends)

Week Twenty-Eight Review

Name

Find the mistakes. Write each sentence correctly on the line.

1. Many people shoose to visit the beash every summer.

2. They place their blanckets on the soft warm sand.

3. If you are lukky, you might find an interesting schell.

4. Surfers add wacks to their boards.

Monthly Review

Name _____

A. Find the mistakes. Write each sentence correctly.

1. the students goes to the Metropolitan museum of Art in new York.

_____

2. Our guide ask us to choos our favorite painting.

_____

3. At first i am not shure how to answer.

_____

4. The picture that stix in my mind is one by pablo picasso.

_____

5. I tells them I feel lukky to have seen that painting.

_____

B. Find a word in the box that rhymes with a word below.

red	orange	yellow	green	blue
purple	gold	brown	white	silver

moo _____   clean _____   rolled _____

noun_____   said _____   light _____

hello _____

Write the three words that did not rhyme on the lines below.

_____   _____   _____

Adjectives

Week Twenty-Nine

1

Name _____

An adjective is a word that describes something. *Smart, green, scary,* or *tasty* describe people, places, or things.

Is it an adjective? Write *Yes* or *No* on the line.

_____ 1. red

_____ 2. small

_____ 3. chair

_____ 4. sloppy

_____ 5. throw

Adjectives

Week Twenty-Nine

2

Name _____

An adjective is a word that describes something. *Smart, green, scary,* or *tasty* describe people, places, or things.

Circle the adjective in each pair.

1.   big   barn

2.   wait   long

3.   wet   floor

4.   old   friend

5.   eat   sweet

Adjectives

Week Twenty-Nine
3

Name

An adjective is a word that describes something. *Smart, green, scary,* or *tasty* describe people, places, or things.

Circle the adjective in each sentence.

1. The horses live in a large stable.

2. Brown saddles hang on the wall.

3. They eat oats from a wooden bucket.

4. One horse makes a loud sound.

5. All of the other horses turn their beautiful heads.

Adjectives

Week Twenty-Nine
4

Name

An adjective is a word that describes something. *Smart, green, scary,* or *tasty* describe people, places, or things.

Circle the adjectives.

1.	little	sharp	needle
2.	see	movie	scary
3.	mountain	tall	dangerous
4.	quiet	nice	good
5.	sticky	soft	rock

Adjectives

Week Twenty-Nine

5

An adjective is a word that describes something. *Smart, green, scary,* or *tasty* describe people, places, or things.

Circle the adjectives.

1. The friendly teacher tells a funny story.

2. Students sit in hard plastic chairs.

3. A huge poster hangs on the green wall.

4. The new sign explains the rules.

5. The bright colors and shapes are pretty.

Adjectives

Week Twenty-Nine Review

Find the adjectives. Write them on the lines.

1. Old stories can be scary.
   _____ _____

2. A story can be long or short.
   _____ _____

3. A good story has interesting characters.
   _____ _____

4. Bright and beautiful pictures can help a story.
   _____ _____

5. When you tell a story, use a loud, clear voice.
   _____ _____

Plural Nouns

Week Thirty 1

Name

Some plural nouns do not follow the regular rules.

Circle the plural nouns.

1. An elephant has four feet.

2. How many teeth does a crocodile have?

3. Geese fly south during the winter.

4. Do mice really like to eat cheese?

5. Many children like to visit the zoo.

Plural Nouns

Week Thirty 2

Name

Some plural nouns do not follow the regular rules.

Write the plural nouns on the lines below.

1. 1 tooth   2 _____

2. 1 mouse   2 _____

3. 1 foot   2 _____

4. 1 child   2 _____

5. 1 goose   2 _____

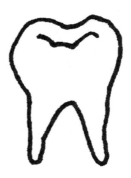

Plural Nouns

Week Thirty **3**

Name _____

Some plural nouns do not follow the regular rules.

Choose the correct word. Write it on the line.

1. Four _____ (men, mans) pick fruits in the field.
2. Some of the _____ (berrys, berries) are ripe.
3. The _____ (cherrys, cherries) are not ready yet.
4. Three _____ (womens, women) feed the animals in the barn.
5. We buy fruit and cakes for two birthday _____ (parties, partys).

Plural Nouns

Week Thirty **4**

Name _____

Some plural nouns do not follow the regular rules.

Write the plural of each noun on the line.

1. penny _____
2. day _____
3. story _____
4. spy _____
5. boy _____

Plural Nouns

Week Thirty 5

Name

Some plural nouns do not follow the regular rules.

Write the plural nouns on the lines.

1. 1 sheep   2 _____

2. 1 person   2 _____

3. 1 bunny   2 _____

4. 1 fish   2 _____

5. 1 fly   2 _____

Plural Nouns

Week Thirty Review

Name

Find the mistakes. Write the correct sentences on the lines.

1. Four childs visit the petting zoo.

_____

2. They see three mouses and a flock of gooses, too.

_____

3. Later, they pet some fluffy sheeps.

_____

4. The mens and womens who work there are very helpful.

_____

Commas

Week Thirty-One

1

Name

Use a comma between a date and a year. *March 4, 2000, is Sara's birthday.*

Circle the correct date.

1. May 26, 1986   May, 26 1986

2. October 18, 1972   October, 18, 1972

3. July, 4 1776   July 4, 1776

4. January 30, 2005   January, 30 2005

5. November 6 2006   November 6, 2006

Commas

Week Thirty-One

2

Name

Use a comma between a date and a year. *March 4, 2000, is Sara's birthday.*

Each date is missing a comma. Write each date correctly on the line.

1. February 2 2006   _____

2. April 5 1998   _____

3. October 13 1952   _____

4. December 16 1825   _____

5. March 20 1988   _____

Commas

Week Thirty-One

3

Name

Use a comma between a day and a month. *Monday, August 15, is Jose's party.*

Circle the correct date.

1. Friday June, 14	Friday, June 14
2. Wednesday, July 8	Wednesday July 8
3. Saturday, May 25	Saturday May 25
4. Thursday October 2	Thursday, October 2
5. Tuesday, August 11	Tuesday August, 11

Commas

Week Thirty-One

4

Name

Use a comma between a day and a month. *Monday, August 15, is Jose's party.*

Each date is missing a comma.
Write each date correctly on the line.

1. Sunday January 11 _____

2. Tuesday June 18 _____

3. Friday November 9 _____

4. Saturday September 27 _____

5. Wednesday August 5 _____

Commas

Week Thirty-One 5

Name

Use a comma between a date and a year. **March 4, 2000, is Sara's birthday.**
Use a comma between a day and a month. **Monday, August 15, is Jose's party.**

Each date is missing a comma.
Write each date correctly on the line.

1. Thursday March 6 _____

2. November 14 1975 _____

3. July 28 2004 _____

4. Wednesday February 28 _____

5. April 30 1865 _____

Commas

Week Thirty-One Review

Name

Find the mistakes. Write each sentence correctly on the line.

1. Congress passed the Declaration of Independence on July 4 1776.

   _____

2. Thomas Jefferson was born on April 13 1743.

   _____

3. A new stamp was issued last year on Friday September 6.

   _____

4. Our class visited City Hall on Monday May 12.

   _____

Spelling (Homophones)

Week Thirty-Two

1

Name

Homophones sound the same. They have different meanings.

Match the homophones.
Draw a line between each pair of homophones.

1.	wear	so
2.	sew	too
3.	bear	meat
4.	two	bare
5.	meet	where

Spelling (Homophones)

Week Thirty-Two

2

Name

Homophones sound the same. They have different meanings.

Write a homophone for each word on the line.
Choose a word from the box.

weight   sun   tale   hear   see

1. sea _____

2. here _____

3. son _____

4. tail _____

5. wait _____

Spelling (Homophones)

Week Thirty-Two

3

Homophones sound the same. They have different meanings.

Write the correct word on the line.

1. Can you _____ (see, sea) the boat?

2. It is floating on the _____ (see, sea).

3. You can _____ (here, hear) the loud horn.

4. The boat will be _____ (here, hear) soon.

5. It will arrive before the _____ (sun, son) sets.

Spelling (Homophones)

Week Thirty-Two

4

Homophones sound the same. They have different meanings.

Write the correct word on the line.

1. You might have to _____ (wait, weight) at the doctor's office.

2. The scale will measure your _____ (wait, weight).

3. The doctor will _____ (wear, where) a white coat.

4. _____ (Wear, Where) is the hospital?

5. The nurse will _____ (meat, meet) you there.

Spelling (Homophones)

Week Thirty-Two

5

Name

Homophones sound the same. They have different meanings.

Write the correct word on the line.

1. Did you read the _____ (tale, tail) about a talking tiger?

2. The tiger has a long and furry _____ (tale, tail).

3. A big _____ (bear, bare) was hiding in the woods.

4. The _____ (too, two) animals talked for hours.

5. Then it got late, _____ (sew, so) the tiger went home.

Spelling (Homophones)

Week Thirty-Two Review

Name

Find the mistakes. Write each sentence correctly on the line.

1. A blue moon happens when there are too full moons in one month.

_____

2. Use the telescope sew you can look at the moon.

_____

3. Weight until the sky is dark.

_____

4. You will be able to sea dark shapes on the moon.

_____

Monthly Review

Name _____

A. Find the mistakes. Write each sentence correctly.

1. Some childs where braces to straighten their tooths.

   _____

2. Braces today come in different colors sizes and shapes.

   _____

3. She will meat a new dentist on Thursday July 17.

   _____

4. He will give her a toothbrush toothpaste and floss.

   _____

B. Find six adjectives in the box. Go across and down.
Write them on the lines.

S	M	A	L	L
I	L	D	A	S
M	N	P	R	O
W	E	T	G	F
S	W	E	E	T

_____   _____

_____   _____

_____   _____

C. Complete this play with words from the box.

    bare   bear   hear   here   too   two   wear   where

Suzi: Did you _____ that? I think it's a _____!

Jake: _____? (A bear appears.)

Bear: I'm over _____.

Suzi and Jake: A A A A A G H !

Bear: (to Jake) May I _____ your hat? My head
feels _____. (Jake and Suzie run away.)

Bear: Oh, well. Those _____ were much _____
jumpy.

Pronouns

Week Thirty-Three

1

Name

A pronoun is a word that replaces a noun. Subject pronouns are *I, you, he, she, it, we,* and *they.*

Write the correct word on the line.

1. _____ (We, Us) went to the aquarium.

2. The guide told _____ (we, us) all about the fish.

3. _____ (They, Them) live in large, beautiful tanks.

4. The guide showed _____ (I, me) the jellyfish.

5. _____ (I, Me) thought they looked very weird.

© Weekly Reader Corp.

Pronouns

Week Thirty-Three

2

Name

A pronoun is a word that replaces a noun. Subject pronouns are *I, you, he, she, it, we,* and *they.* Object pronouns are *me, you, him, her, it, us,* and *them.*

Choose a word from the box to complete each sentence. Write it on the line.

we   us   me   they   she

1. Our teacher showed _____ how to read a compass.

2. _____ gave each team a compass.

3. _____ were fun to use.

4. _____ found out that our room faces east.

5. My father gave _____ another lesson at home.

© Weekly Reader Corp.

Pronouns

Week Thirty-Three

3

Name

A pronoun is a word that replaces a noun. Possessive pronouns show ownership.

Write the correct word on the line.

1. The mayor gave _____ (her, she) speech at noon.
2. She announced _____ (her, she) plans for a new playground.
3. Then our principal gave _____ (him, his) support.
4. The listeners clapped _____ (them, their) hands.
5. We look forward to _____ (us, our) new place to play.

Pronouns

Week Thirty-Three

4

Name

A pronoun is a word that replaces a noun. Subject pronouns are *I, you, he, she, it, we,* and *they.* Object pronouns are *me, you, him, her, it, us,* and *them.* Possessive pronouns show ownership.

Write a word from the box to complete each sentence.

I   me   her   it   mine

1. That painting is _____ .
2. I painted _____ last week.
3. Ms. Juarez showed _____ how to mix colors.
4. _____ plan to give it to my aunt.
5. She will probably hang it on _____ refrigerator.

Pronouns

Week Thirty-Three

5

Name _____

A pronoun is a word that replaces a noun. Possessive pronouns show ownership.

Write the correct word on the line.

1. Betsy Ross sewed _____ (her, hers) famous flag in 1776.

2. _____ (It, Its) had 13 stars.

3. _____ (They, Them) were white on a blue square.

4. She sewed _____ (them, their) on by hand.

5. Today, there are 50 stars on _____ (ours, our) flag.

Pronouns

Week Thirty-Three Review

Name _____

Find the mistakes. Write each sentence correctly on the line.

1. Us give reports about ours favorite people in sports.

   _____

2. Me friend Archie tells we about Joe Namath.

   _____

3. Him was a famous football player for the New York Jets.

   _____

4. Me show they a poster of five baseball players.

   _____

5. Them are all in the Baseball Hall of Fame.

   _____

Capitalization

Week Thirty-Four 1

Name

Capitalize days of the week and months of the year.

Circle the correct word.

1. Monday   monday

2. April   april

3. Sunday   sunday

4. thursday   Thursday

5. january   January

Capitalization

Week Thirty-Four 2

Name

Capitalize days of the week and months of the year.

Circle the word that needs a capital letter. Write it on the line.

1. On saturday the school held a poetry workshop.

_____

2. In october we will publish a collection of poems.

_____

3. A famous poet visited our class last may.

_____

4. One student wrote about snow in july.

_____

Capitalization

Week Thirty-Four 3

Name

Capitalize days of the week and months of the year.

Circle the word that needs a capital letter. Write it on the line.

1. Many trees have no leaves in december.
   _____

2. On monday we saw a beautiful evergreen.
   _____

3. What plants are still growing in february?
   _____

4. Some bulbs begin to grow in march.

   _____

Capitalization

Week Thirty-Four 4

Name

Capitalize days of the week and months of the year.

Circle the correct word.

1. tuesday   Tuesday

2. June   june

3. August   august

4. november   November

5. Saturday   saturday

Capitalization

Week Thirty-Four 5

Name

Capitalize days of the week and months of the year.

**Circle the word that needs a capital letter.
Write it on the line.**

1. The school year begins in september.
   _____

2. On thursday we have music class.
   _____

3. We have a guest teacher every monday.
   _____

4. The school talent show happens in january.
   _____

Capitalization

Week Thirty-Four Review

Name

Find the mistakes. Write each sentence correctly on the line.

1. A family began a cross-country trip on tuesday, june 27.
   _____

2. On wednesday, july 5, they reached the Mississippi River.
   _____

3. They reached Kansas about a week later on a friday.
   _____

4. On tuesday, august 1, they crossed the border
   of California.
   _____

Apostrophes

Week Thirty-Five 1

Name

Use apostrophes in possessive nouns and contractions.

Circle the correct word.

1.	would'nt	wouldn't
2.	cat'n	can't
3.	wont	won't
4.	mens	men's
5.	mice's	mices

Apostrophes

Week Thirty-Five 2

Name

Use apostrophes in possessive nouns and contractions.

One word is missing an apostrophe. Write it correctly on the line.

1. My sister didnt find out about the surprise party.

   _____

2. Most of my sisters friends were very quiet.

   _____

3. The childrens giggles almost gave it away.

   _____

4. Shell be harder to fool next year.

   _____

Apostrophes

Week Thirty-Five

3

Name

Use apostrophes in possessive nouns and contractions.

Circle the correct word.

1.   it's   its'

2.   thats   that's

3.   theyre   they're

4.   was'nt   wasn't

5.   shouldn't   shouldnt

Apostrophes

Week Thirty-Five

4

Name

Use apostrophes in possessive nouns and contractions.

One word is missing an apostrophe. Write it correctly on the line.

1. The fishs water is very cloudy.

_____

2. The aquariums walls are covered in algae.

_____

3. We havent cleaned it this week.

_____

4. It is Dads turn to clean it next week.

_____

Apostrophes

Week Thirty-Five

5

Name

Use apostrophes in possessive nouns and contractions.

One word is missing an apostrophe. Write it correctly on the line.

1. Cats arent supposed to like dogs.

   _____

2. However, my grandfathers pets get along together.

   _____

3. The new kitten isnt at all afraid of the big dog.

   _____

4. The dogs mouth is as big as the whole cat.

   _____

Apostrophes

Week Thirty-Five Review

Name

Find the mistakes. Write the sentence correctly on the line.

1. I wouldnt like to be a fish.

   _____

2. Im pretty sure that a fishs life would be scary.

   _____

3. I cant think of anything scarier than a sharks teeth's.

   _____

4. It would be especially awful if youre the size of a single tooth.

   _____

Spelling (Commonly Misspelled Words)

Week Thirty-Six   1

Name _____

Some words have tricky spelling patterns.

Arrange the letters to spell a word.

1. R E W E   ___ ___ ___ ___

2. P N U O   ___ ___ ___ ___

3. O E M S   ___ ___ ___ ___

4. L D O C U   ___ ___ ___ ___ ___ ___

5. H I T E R   ___ ___ ___ ___ ___ ___

Spelling (Commonly Misspelled Words)

Week Thirty-Six   2

Name _____

Some words have tricky spelling patterns.

Circle the correct spelling.

1. becuz   because

2. friend   freind

3. clothes   clothz

4. littel   little

5. write   wryt

Spelling (Commonly Misspelled Words)

Week Thirty-Six

3

Name

Some words have tricky spelling patterns.

Circle the word that is NOT spelled correctly. Write the correct spelling on the line.

1. Do you knowe how icicles start?

   _____

2. They form wen water drips and then freezes.

   _____

3. Some icicles hang down from beelow a roof.

   _____

4. Look up abuv to see if there's an icicle.

   _____

Spelling (Commonly Misspelled Words)

Week Thirty-Six

4

Name

Some words have tricky spelling patterns.

Write the correct word on the line.

1. The students play a game at _____.
   (skool, school).

2. They all sit in a _____ and listen carefully.
   (circle, cirkel)

3. The first player whispers a sentence just _____
   to the next person.   (onse, once)

4. The sentence goes _____ the group.
   (around, arownd)

Spelling (Commonly Misspelled Words)

Week Thirty-Six

5

Name

Some words have tricky spelling patterns.

Circle the word that is NOT spelled correctly.
Write the correct spelling on the line.

1. some   favorit   their   _____

2. woulde   circle   around   _____

3. when   were   beautifle   _____

4. above   below   pleaze   _____

Spelling (Commonly Misspelled Words)

Week Thirty-Six Review

Name

Find the mistakes. Write each sentence correctly.

1. Many stories begin "Onse up on a time."

   _____

2. Sum of our favorit stories are about frends.

   _____

3. Our skool has a lot of books in the library.

   _____

4. Pleaze ask befor you borrow one of the books.

   _____

5. What wood you like to wryte about?

Monthly Review

Name

A. Find the mistakes. Write each sentence correctly.

1. One tuesday last month us learned a new song.

   _____

2. The song wasnt hard for we to sing.

   _____

3. Ours class will perform the song for parents this april.

   _____

4. Dont you think it's fun to sing your favorit songs?

   _____

5. Arownd december, many people like to sing holiday songs.

   _____

B. Write the answers in the puzzle.

Across
1. you wear them
2. opposite of below
4. very pretty
7. more than none
9. pal; buddy
10. where you go to learn

Down
1. shape of a coin
2. one more time
3. opposite of inside
5. a polite word
6. opposite of above
8. small

Daily Language Practice
Answers — Grade 2

Week 1
Day One
1. tan 2. sand 3. last 4. fan 5. lamp
Day Two
1. get 2. When 3. set 4. west
5. fell
Day Three
1. win 2. fit 3. trip 4. crib 5. brick
Day Four
1. hop 2. trot 3. lot 4. pond 5. rock
Day Five
1. bug 2. sun 3. must 4. truck
5. fun
Review
1. when, fell 2. bug, truck
3. rock, trot 4. sand, fan 5. trip, fit

Week 2
Day One
1. period 2. question mark
3. question mark 4. period
5. period
Day Two
1. The 2. It 3. Who 4. In 5. Light
Day Three
1. question mark 2. period 3. period
4. question mark 5. period
Day Four
1. Apples are fruits that grow on
trees. 2. Apple trees grow from
seeds. 3. Where can you find the
roots of a tree? 4. Why do apples
float? 5. They float because they
contain air.
Day Five
1. Some Native Americans fished
for food. 2. Many Native
Americans made baskets for
storage. 3. What were tepees?
4. Tepees are cone-shaped homes
made with tree bark.
Review
1. Scorpions have fangs and
stingers. 2. Where do most
scorpions live? 3. They live in
deserts around the world. 4. How
many legs does a scorpion have?
5. A scorpion has eight legs.

Week 3
Day One
1. ball 2. house 3. water 4. brain
5. friend

Day Two
1. candle, wax 2. flame 3. cakes,
candles 4. matches 5. fire
Day Three
1. No 2. Yes 3. Yes 4. Yes 5. No
Day Four
1. clam, shell 2. crab, Pacific
Ocean 3. Cape Cod, river, boat
4. Miami Beach 5. rock, pebble,
stone
Day Five
1. People, park 2. Wind, trees
3. leaves, ground 4. workers, rakes
5. paths
Review
1. zipper 2. inventor, Gideon
Sundback 3. man, Canada
4. Zippers, buttons 5. pants,
jackets, coats, zippers

Week 4
Day One
1. map, cap 2. dog, log 3. sun, run
4. sky, why 5. trip, ship
Day Two
1. Yes 2. No 3. Yes 4. Yes 5. No
Day Three
1. wish 2. cave 3. spill 4. rope
5. mess
Day Four
1. fox, box 2. grade, made 3. ring,
sing 4. cuts, nuts 5. bend, send
Day Five
1. chick, brick 2. bell, spell 3. near,
hear 4. moon, soon 5. late, plate
Review
1. moon, soon 2. why, sky
3. ring, sing 4. hope, rope
5. sun, run

Month 1 Review
A 1. Do you know what Kwanzaa
is? 2. It is an African American
holiday. 3. Kwanzaa lasts for seven
nights. 4. What do people do
during this holiday? 5. They share
food, stories, and traditions.
B. tree, rabbit, river, cherry, egg
C. 1. will 2. yes 3. yell 4. wish
5. pool

Week 5
Day One
1. date 2. game 3. rain 4. plane
5. eight

Day Two
1. team 2. field 3. green 4. each
5. see
Day Three
1. fine 2. light 3. ride 4. why 5. lie
Day Four
1. road 2. home 3. show 4. tow
5. go
Day Five
1. mule 2. spoon 3. rude
4. moon 5. blue
Review
1. game, date 2. spoon, noon
3. home, hole 4. team, stream
5. ride, time

Week 6
Day One
1. Plants, roots 2. Leaves, stems
3. Fruits, vegetables, seeds
4. Gardens 5. winds, crops
Day Two
1. stars 2. planets 3. moons
4. rockets 5. comets
Day Three
1. beaches 2. tides 3. bushes
4. plants 5. shells
Day Four
1. homes 2. schools 3. churches
4. classes 5. buildings
Day Five
1. dresses 2. Tailors
3. patterns, dozens, pieces
4. machines 5. touches, buttons,
ribbons, bows
Review
1. bushes 2. machines 3. buildings
4. stars 5. churches

Week 7
Day One
1. An 2. A 3. An 4. a
Day Two
1. a 2. an 3. a 4. An 5. a
Day Three
1. An elephant is a mammal.
2. All mammals have a backbone.
3. An eel is not a mammal.
4. It is a kind of fish.
Day Four
1. A, a 2. an 3. A 4. a
Day Five
1. a 2. a, a 3. an 4. a 5. An

Day Five
1. has 2. have 3. have 4. has
Review
1. Stars shine in the night sky.
2. The moon looks full tonight.
3. Saturn has a huge ring.
4. The planets are very far away.
5. The sun rises in the morning.

Week 15
Day One
1. Yes 2. Yes 3. No 4. Yes 5. No
Day Two
1. Bees live in hives. 2. The queen bee lays eggs. 3. Some bees make honey. 4. A female honeybee dies when it stings. 5. Bees are fuzzy.
Day Three
1. Yes 2. Yes 3. No 4. No 5. No
Day Four
Answers will vary. Possible answers: 1. takes a picture 2. A chorus 3. finishes a painting 4. A telephone 5. moves around the sun
Day Five
1. No 2. No 3. No 4. No 5. Yes
Review
1. The Pilgrims celebrated the first Thanksgiving. 2. We eat a big meal. 3. Some people like to watch a colorful parade. 4. Football players appear on television. 5. Families around the country share their food.

Week 16
Day One
1. green 2. mean 3. three 4. deep 5. ice cream
Day Two
1. why 2. like 3. high 4. size 5. might
Day Three
1. sleep 2. night 3. dream 4. need 5. time
Day Four
1. pie 2. eyes 3. leaf 4. feel 5. bright
Day Five
1. lime 2. trees 3. ripe 4. squeeze 5. peel
Review
1. Why do we have eyes? 2. They help you see the world around you. 3. Your sight is stronger during the day than at night. 4. Some people need glasses to see things far away. 5. Other people use glasses to read books and magazines.

Month 4 Review
A. 1. New York City is the largest city in the United States. 2. About eight million people live there. 3. At night lights shine in Times Square. 4. The Empire State Building has 102 stories. 5. Central Park is a huge green space in the middle of the city.
B. Across 1. tree 3. high 5. leaf 8. sleep **Down** 2. right 4. green 6. feel 7. time

Week 17
Day One
1. D 2. E 3. C 4. A 5. B
Day Two
1. a book's cover 2. a chair's leg 3. a teacher's class 4. a pencil's point 5. a friend's smile
Day Three
1. turtle's 2. museum's 3. egg's 4. Jane's 5. story's
Day Four
1. a volcano's lava 2. a cliff's edge 3. a mountain's peak 4. a river's current 5. a waterfall's roar
Day Five
1. Japan's 2. Tokyo's 3. city's 4. subway's
Review
1. The scientist heard a loud bird's quack. 2. She found an egg near the pond's edge. 3. The egg's shell was spotted brown and white. 4. A duck's feathers are waterproof. 5. A swan's feathers are usually black or white.

Week 18
Day One
1. talking 2. finding 3. thinking 4. teaching 5. wandering
Day Two
1. leaning 2. falling 3. standing 4. looking 5. discussing
Day Three
1. baking 2. hiking 3. smiling 4. wiggling 5. preparing
Day Four
1. racing 2. taking 3. hoping 4. changing 5. announcing
Day Five
1. winning 2. stopping 3. swimming 4. knitting 5. rubbing
Review
1. The director is making a new movie. 2. She is telling the actors where to move. 3. The actors are listening carefully. 4. People are stopping to watch the crew. 5. Soon, the audience is clapping very loudly.

Week 19
Day One
1. armor 2. castle 3. knight 4. moat 5. queen
Day Two
1. Yes 2. No 3. No 4. Yes 5. Yes
Day Three
1. poppy 2. rose 3. sunflower 4. tulip 5. violet
Day Four
1. opal 2. silver 3. emerald 4. topaz 5. copper
Day Five
1. jaguar 2. leopard 3. lion 4. lynx 5. tiger
Review
1. bird, fish, snake 2. blue, green, orange, purple, red, yellow 3. paper, pencil, poem 4. Earth, Jupiter, Mars, Mercury, Neptune, Pluto, Saturn, Uranus, Venus

Week 20
Day One
1. home 2. coat 3. boats 4. float 5. throw
Day Two
1. moon 2. rude 3. broom 4. threw 5. spoon
Day Three
1. tune 2. notes 3. group 4. blow
Day Four
1. know 2. toe 3. soup 4. room 5. few
Day Five
1. roads 2. below 3. to 4. you
Review
1. In spring, many flowers begin to grow. 2. Summer begins in June each year. 3. A blue moon happens when there are two full moons in one month. 4. In fall, winds blow and leaves float down.

Month 5 Review
A. 1. A student is writing about famous people's houses. 2. She is keeping notes about what she reads. 3. She is planning to write about a president's childhood. 4. Abraham Lincoln's first home was in Kentucky. 5. It was a log cabin that had only one room.
B. cobra, elephant, falcon, gecko, locust, mongoose, plover, spider, turtle; the back cover

Week 21
Day One
1. Yes 2. Yes 3. No 4. Yes 5. Yes

Day Two
1. long, short 2. easy, hard 3. thick, thin 4. inside, outside 5. clean, dirty

Day Three
1. small 2. start 3. soft
4. sloppy 5. sour

Day Four
Answers will vary. Possible answers:
1. short 2. cheap 3. new 4. white

Day Five
1. fast, slow 2. asleep, awake
3. empty, full 4. dull, interesting
5. above, below

Review
1. short, long 2. empty, full 3. stop, start 4. below, above 5. fresh, stale

Week 22

Day One
1. isn't 2. You'll 3. you'd
4. aren't 5. I'm

Day Two
1. couldn't 2. can't 3. isn't
4. aren't 5. won't

Day Three
1. does not 2. you are 3. she will
4. did not 5. he is

Day Four
1. didn't 2. She's 3. won't
4. it's 5. He'll

Day Five
1. I'm 2. she's 3. they're
4. we'll 5. wouldn't

Review
1. We'll go to the museum tomorrow. 2. It isn't very far away.
3. The tour won't take more than one hour. 4. Aren't you looking forward to the trip?

Week 23

Day One
1. walked 2. played 3. laughed
4. visited 5. collected

Day Two
1. invented 2. started 3. listened
4. helped 5. learned

Day Three
1. liked 2. studied 3. saved
4. carried 5. copied

Day Four
1. married 2. lived 3. nicknamed
4. tried

Day Five
1. stopped 2. hurried 3. stirred
4. planned 5. worried

Review
1. A streetcar was trapped under a heavy snowfall. 2. The riders worried about what would happen.
3. The rescue team hurried to the scene. 4. They arrived minutes later.

Week 24

Day One
1. swimmer 2. counter 3. player
4. nicer 5. ruler

Day Two
1. form 2. pour 3. shore 4. board
5. floor

Day Three
1. weather 2. more
3. stores 4. warm

Day Four
1. bird 2. dollar 3. feather
4. earth 5. motor

Day Five
1. girls 2. First 3. court 4. lawyer

Review
1. The girl makes a beautiful new skirt. 2. She puts the fabric on the floor. 3. Her brother helps a little, too. 4. He holds the ruler while she cuts the cloth. 5. Sometimes four hands are better than two.

Month 6 Review

A. 1. Helen Keller couldn't see or hear. 2. Helen's family lived in Alabama. 3. At first, they didn't think Helen would ever communicate.
4. Then Anne Sullivan helped her learn. 5. The two friends traveled together for many years.
B. hot, cold; large, small; fast, slow; sit, stand; begin, end
C. dollar, thunder, girl, world, nurse

Week 25

Day One
1. Mrs. Chen 2. New Mexico
3. Mount Everest 4. Lake Erie
5. Fifth Avenue

Day Two
1. Rudolph 2. four 3. Later
4. States

Day Three
1. March 2. Angeles
3. Where 4. Dakota

Day Four
1. Fort Knox 2. Pacific Ocean
3. John Smith 4. King Tut
5. South Carolina

Day Five
1. I 2. Arthur 3. Britain 4. Brave

Review
1. Four presidents' faces are carved into Mount Rushmore. 2. On the left, you can see George Washington. 3. On the right, you will find Theodore Roosevelt .
4. This famous mountain is near Keystone, South Dakota.

Week 26

Day One
1. grow 2. pick 3. carries
4. sells 5. eat

Day Two
1. ring 2. rings 3. practice
4. hear 5. sings

Day Three
1. helps 2. learn 3. is 4. are 5. try

Day Four
1. crash 2. sinks 3. makes 4. is

Day Five
1. spin 2. catches 3. has
4. do 5. have

Review
1. Stars are very far away. 2. The moon travels around Earth. 3. Our galaxy has many stars and planets.
4. A constellation is a group of stars.

Week 27

Day One
1. Yes 2. Yes 3. No 4. No 5. Yes

Day Two
1. cheer, near 2. real, feel 3. grow, toe 4. much, touch 5. laugh, half

Day Three
1. state 2. grows 3. rain 4. hour
5. bees

Day Four
1. booth, truth 2. sew, know 3. lake, steak 4. new, true 5. fuzz, was

Day Five
1. stare, hair 2. food, rude 3. mix, sticks 4. wait, plate 5. boys, noise

Review
1. rude, food 2. please, bees
3. store, four 4. know, sew
5. boys, noise

Week 28

Day One
1. blanket 2. fork 3. bucket
4. lucky 5. circle

Day Two
1. white 2. choose 3. wind
4. sure 5. wheel

Day Three
1. bridge 2. stage 3. edge 4. badge

Day Four
1. box 2. blocks 3. checks 4. wax
5. sticks

Day Five
1. match 2. beach 3. itch 4. bench
5. peach

Review
1. Many people choose to visit the beach every summer. 2. They place their blankets on the soft warm sand.
3. If you are lucky, you might find an interesting shell. 4. Surfers add wax to their boards.

Month 7 Review

A. 1. The students go to the Metropolitan Museum of Art in New York. 2. Our guide asks us to choose our favorite painting. 3. At first I am not sure how to answer. 4. The picture that sticks in my mind is one by Pablo Picasso. 5. I tell them I feel lucky to have seen that painting.

B. blue, green, gold, brown, red, white, yellow
Orange, purple, and silver have no rhymes.

Week 29

Day One
1. Yes 2. Yes 3. No 4. Yes 5. No

Day Two
1. big 2. long 3. wet 4. old 5. sweet

Day Three
1. large 2. Brown 3. wooden 4. loud 5. beautiful

Day Four
1. little, sharp 2. scary 3. tall, dangerous 4. quiet, nice, good 5. sticky, soft

Day Five
1. friendly, funny 2. hard, plastic 3. huge, green 4. new 5. bright, pretty

Review
1. Old, scary 2. long, short 3. good, interesting 4. Bright, beautiful 5. loud, clear

Week 30

Day One
1. feet 2. teeth 3. Geese 4. mice 5. children

Day Two
1. teeth 2. mice 3. feet 4. children 5. geese

Day Three
1. men 2. berries 3. cherries 4. women 5. parties

Day Four
1. pennies 2. days 3. stories 4. spies 5. boys

Day Five
1. sheep 2. people 3. bunnies 4. fish 5. flies

Review
1. Four children visit the petting zoo. 2. They see three mice and a flock of geese, too. 3. Later, they pet some fluffy sheep. 4. The men and women who work there are very helpful.

Week 31

Day One
1. May 26, 1986 2. October 18, 1972 3. July 4, 1776 4. January 30, 2005 5. November 6, 2006

Day Two
1. February 2, 2006 2. April 5, 1998 3. October 13, 1952 4. December 16, 1825 5. March 20, 1988

Day Three
1. Friday, June 14 2. Wednesday, July 8 3. Saturday, May 25 4. Thursday, October 2 5. Tuesday, August 11

Day Four
1. Sunday, January 11 2. Tuesday, June 18 3. Friday, November 9 4. Saturday, September 27 5. Wednesday, August 5

Day Five
1. Thursday, March 6 2. November 14, 1975 3. July 28, 2004 4. Wednesday, February 28 5. April 30, 1865

Review
1. Congress passed the Declaration of Independence on July 4, 1776. 2. Thomas Jefferson was born on April 13, 1743. 3. A new stamp was issued last year on Friday, September 6. 4. Our class visited City Hall on Monday, May 12.

Week 32

Day One
1. wear, where 2. sew, so 3. bear, bare 4. two, too 5. meet, meat

Day Two
1. see 2. hear 3. sun 4. tale 5. weight

Day Three
1. see 2. sea 3. hear 4. here 5. sun

Day Four
1. wait 2. weight 3. wear 4. Where 5. meet

Day Five
1. tale 2. tail 3. bear 4. two 5. so

Review
1. A blue moon happens when there are two full moons in one month. 2. Use the telescope so you can look at the moon. 3. Wait until the sky is dark. 4. You will be able to see dark shapes on the moon.

Month 8 Review

A. 1. Some children wear braces to straighten their teeth. 2. Braces today come in different colors, sizes, and shapes. 3. She will meet a new dentist on Thursday, July 17. 4. He will give her a toothbrush, toothpaste, and floss.

B. small, wet, sweet, new, large, soft

C. hear, bear, Where, here, wear, bare, two, too

Week 33

Day One
1. We 2. us 3. They 4. me 5. I

Day Two
1. us 2. She 3. They 4. We 5. me

Day Three
1. her 2. her 3. his 4. their 5. our

Day Four
1. mine 2. it 3. me 4. I 5. her

Day Five
1. her 2. It 3. They 4. them 5. our

Review
1. We give reports about our favorite people in sports. 2. My friend Archie tells us about Joe Namath. 3. He was a famous football player for the New York Jets. 4. I show them a poster of five baseball players. 5. They are all in the Baseball Hall of Fame.

Week 34

Day One
1. Monday 2. April 3. Sunday 4. Thursday 5. January

Day Two
1. Saturday 2. October 3. May 4. July

Day Three
1. December 2. Monday 3. February 4. March

Day Four
1. Tuesday 2. June 3. August 4. November 5. Saturday

Day Five
1. September 2. Thursday 3. Monday 4. January

Review
1. The family began a cross-country trip on Tuesday, June 27. 2. On Wednesday, July 5, they reached the Mississippi River. 3. They reached Kansas about a week later on a Friday. 4. On Tuesday, August 1, they crossed the border of California.

Week 35

Day One
1. wouldn't 2. can't 3. won't 4. men's 5. mice's

Day Two
1. didn't 2. sister's 3. children's 4. She'll

Day Three
1. it's 2. that's 3. they're 4. wasn't
5. shouldn't

Day Four
1. fish's 2. aquarium's 3. haven't
4. Dad's

Day Five
1. aren't 2. grandfather's
3. isn't 4. dog's

Review
1. I wouldn't like to be a fish.
2. I'm pretty sure that a fish's life
would be scary. 3. I can't think of
anything scarier than a shark's
teeth. 4. It would be especially
awful if you're the size of a single
tooth.

Week 36
Day One
1. were 2. upon 3. some
4. could 5. their

Day Two
1. because 2. friend 3. clothes
4. little 5. write

Day Three
1. know 2. when 3. below 4. above

Day Four
1. school 2. circle 3. once 4. around

Day Five
1. favorite 2. would
3. beautiful 4. please

Review
1. Many stories begin "Once upon
a time." 2. Some of our favorite
stories are about friends. 3. Our
school has a lot of books in the
library. 4. Please ask before you
borrow one of the books. 5. What
would you like to write about?

Month 9 Review
A. 1. One Tuesday last month we
learned a new song. 2. The song
wasn't hard for us to sing. 3. Our
class will perform the song for
parents this April. 4. Don't you
think it's fun to sing your favorite
songs? · 5. Around December, many
people like to sing holiday songs.
B.
Across

1. clothes	7. some
2. above	9. friend
4. beautiful	10. school

Down

1. circle	5. please
2. again	6. below
3. outside	8. little